WORDBUILD FOUNDAT

When you were a very young person, you made up words like *choo-choo*, *boo-boo*, and *kitty-cat*. Later, names like *Superman* and *Wonderwoman* and *Spiderman* became familiar. You probably didn't realize it at the time, but you were building compound words.

It was fun when you figured out that you could take one word and build lots of compound words with it, like *treehouse*, *birdhouse*, and *doghouse*, or *eyebrow*, *eyeball*, and *eyelash*. It is interesting that the first part of a compound word many times is a type of the second part of the word – a treehouse, a birdhouse and a doghouse are all types of houses.

When you looked a little closer, you saw that there are different relationships between the two parts of compound words. For example, a *treehouse* is a house IN a tree, but a *doghouse* is a house FOR a dog.

Your next adventure with words uses the same idea of putting together two pieces to make up a new word, but this time one of the pieces is usually *not* a word all by itself. These kinds of word pieces are called *prefixes* and *suffixes* – things that you can stick on the front or the back of a word you know and make a new word. Even though most prefixes and suffixes are not words by themselves, they *mean* something.

The really neat thing is that when you learn, for example, that the prefix *un* means *not* or *opposite of,* it always means *not* or *opposite of* when you attach it to another word!

Here is a new word for you: **MORPHEME**

A morpheme is the smallest part of a word that *means something*. By the end of this school year, you will be an expert on morphemes!

PREFIX SQUARE

for **over-** meaning "above or too much"

Start in the middle square with the prefix **over** and combine this part with the words in the other squares to build new words. Write each word and a definition you can think of for it in the spaces provided at the bottom of the page.

view	paid	pass
sized	**over-**	ripe
hang	look	coat

AFFIX ADDER

The prefix over- means "above or too much."

1. Write **over** in the blank space in front of each word listed below and make a new word.
2. Tell what you think the new word means.
3. Write a sentence using the new word.

We've done one for you:

FEED means to give food to
...so OVERFEED means to give too much food to.

Sentence: That dog would not be so fat if its owners didn't overfeed it.

____

1. LOAD means to put into
...so ______load means ______________________________
Used in a sentence:

____

2. COAT means a covering
...so ______COAT means ______________________________
Used in a sentence:

____

3. PAY means to give money in return for something
...so ______PAY means ______________________________
Used in a sentence:

____

4. LEAP means to jump across
...so ______LEAP means ______________________________
Used in a sentence:

____

5. TIME means a period measured in hours or other units

...so ______TIME means ____

Used in a sentence:

6. ACHIEVE means to meet a goal

...so ______ACHIEVE means ____________________________________

Used in a sentence:

7. FILL means to supply with as much as can be held

...so ______FILL means ____

Used in a sentence:

8. DRESS means to put on clothes

...so ______DRESS means ______________________________________

Used in a sentence:

9. DONE means cooked

...so ______DONE means _______________________________________

Used in a sentence:

10. DUE means payable now

...so ______DUE means ____

Used in a sentence:

MAGIC SQUARE

for **over**- meaning "above or too much"

Select the best definition for each of the words in the **over** family. Put the number of the definition in the proper space in the Magic Square box. If the numbers going up and down and the numbers going across all add up to the same thing, you have found the magic number!

WORDS

A. overjoyed
B. overpay
C. overcoat
D. overhang
E. overlook
F. overtime
G. overstep
H. overfeed
I. overdress

DEFINITIONS

1. to look at from above
2. an outer piece of clothing
3. to give more than normal amount of food
4. to extend beyond and above
5. to go beyond a limit
6. more than the normal hours of work
7. to give more money than was charged
8. to fail to see
9. very, very happy
10. to wear fancier clothes than expected

Magic Square Box

A.	B.	C.
D.	E.	F.
G.	H.	I.

Magic Number ______

Name ______________________

WORD SEARCH

Words with the prefix over- meaning "above or too much"

Find and circle the words in the grid. Words can go across or up and down, straight or diagonally, forwards or backwards

P	L	K	T	K	D	O	Y	O	V	E	R	L	O	O	K	T	N
D	Q	X	T	O	V	E	R	J	O	Y	E	D	K	L	X	K	K
L	E	G	K	E	D	C	O	P	R	B	N	M	C	T	K	N	G
Z	P	S	R	T	L	V	E	B	V	O	N	Z	R	D	K	N	L
T	L	R	U	Y	E	T	P	M	P	Q	V	L	D	P	A	R	B
M	U	C	X	R	S	D	A	Q	O	G	Y	E	R	H	N	F	F
N	T	K	T	R	E	C	X	O	T	V	G	X	R	C	B	L	V
O	L	I	E	R	O	V	K	J	C	A	E	E	T	L	R	P	X
V	M	V	L	M	F	V	O	T	R	R	V	R	K	W	A	Z	D
E	O	V	L	T	O	M	E	E	C	O	E	L	R	E	Y	P	V
R	N	Z	I	C	V	R	V	R	K	M	N	V	Y	I	L	X	K
S	L	M	F	A	E	O	K	H	D	R	P	J	O	V	P	X	M
H	K	V	R	R	R	M	R	W	X	R	M	N	M	R	Z	E	N
O	H	Y	E	E	P	T	M	T	H	G	I	S	R	E	V	O	N
E	N	K	V	V	A	Z	F	M	L	M	K	V	K	V	Y	L	P
S	W	Y	O	O	Y	P	Q	F	P	Z	M	R	E	O	G	P	T
D	E	K	R	O	W	R	E	V	O	O	V	E	R	F	E	E	D
V	Z	Y	W	R	N	M	O	V	E	R	D	R	E	S	S	E	D

overact
overaged
overcoat
overdressed
overdrive
overfeed
overfill
overhang
overjoyed
overlap
overlook
overpay
overripe
overrun
overshoes
oversight
overstep
overtime
overused
overview
overworked

ENOUGH ALREADY!

Fill in the blanks using the words at the bottom of the page that all mean "above or too much of something."
Why do they mean above or too much of something? _____ ____________________

1. Arnie's book was ________________ at the library, so he had to pay a fine.
2. Students can walk safely across the road using the paved ________________.
3. Slang phrases become ________________ and grow out of style quickly.
4. Even with a wool ________________, Marsha felt the icy wind blowing.
5. If you ________________ the roasting turkey, it will be dry and unfit to eat.
6. The veterinarian told Joanie not to ______________ her already overweight cat.
7. The tired leaf-blowing crew felt ________________ and underpaid.
8. The ________________ bananas had become dark and smelly.
9. The teacher's clear ________________ of what we will be studying helps us learn.
10. The exciting soccer game went into ________________ as the teams tied.

Check off these words as you use them.

overcoat	overcook	overdue	overfeed	overpass
overripe	overtime	overused	overview	overworked

PREFIX SQUARE

for **under**- meaning "below or not enough"

Start in the middle square with the prefix **under** and combine this part with the words in the other squares to build new words. Write each word and a definition you can think of for it in the spaces provided at the bottom of the page.

world	paid	pass
sized	**under-**	brush
foot	powered	coat

____

____

____

____

____

____

____

____

AFFIX ADDER

The prefix under- means "below or not enough."

1. Write **under** in the blank space in front of each word listed below and make a new word.
2. Tell what you think the new word means.
3. Write a sentence using the new word.

We've done one for you:

POWERED means has an engine
... so UNDERPOWERED means has an engine with not enough power.

Sentence: You can't win a NASCAR race with an underpowered car.

1. PASS means a route from one place to another
...so ______PASS means ______________________________
Used in a sentence:

2. EAT means to take food into the body
...so ______EAT means ______________________________
Used in a sentence:

3. PAY means to give money for a job done
...so ______PAY means ______________________________
Used in a sentence:

4. LINE means to insert marks across a page
...so ______LINE means ______________________________
Used in a sentence:

5. SHIRT means a garment for the upper body
...so ______SHIRT means ____
Used in a sentence:

6. ACHIEVE means to meet a goal
...so ______ACHIEVE means ____
Used in a sentence:

7. BRUSH means scrub plants in the woods or to scrub
...so ______BRUSH means ____
Used in a sentence:

8. STATE means to say
...so ______STATE means ____
Used in a sentence:

9. DONE means cooked
...so ______DONE means ____
Used in a sentence:

10. AGE means how old a person or thing is
...so ______AGE means ____
Used in a sentence:

MAGIC SQUARE

for **under**- meaning "below or not enough"

Select the best definition for each of the words in the **under** family. Put the number of the definition in the proper space in the Magic Square box. If the numbers going up and down and the numbers going across all add up to the same thing, you have found the magic number!

WORDS

A. underage
B. undercoat
C. undersell
D. undereat
E. undertow
F. undersized
G. underdone
H. underline
I. underused

DEFINITIONS

1. to begin a project
2. not old enough
3. not utilized enough
4. the pull of water beneath the surface
5. to make a mark below
6. to take in less food than needed
7. to take less for the same product than another seller does
8. smaller than what is necessary
9. the covering beneath the top layer
10. not cooked enough

Magic Square Box

A.	B.	C.
D.	E.	F.
G.	H.	I.

Magic Number ______

Name ______________________

WORD SEARCH

Words with the prefix under- meaning "below or not enough"

Find and circle the words in the grid. Words can go across or up and down, straight or diagonally, forwards or backwards

Q	U	N	D	E	R	L	I	N	E	Z	F	M	U	T	U	Y	N
F	R	R	U	N	D	E	R	A	R	M	T	N	M	N	N	J	F
N	E	U	F	U	M	K	L	L	P	H	D	Y	D	T	R	P	D
D	K	P	N	N	M	P	L	G	Q	E	K	E	Q	V	A	E	M
E	A	F	G	D	Y	R	R	L	R	C	R	P	R	L	R	R	U
S	T	C	N	E	E	Z	Q	T	M	C	R	Y	R	E	W	N	K
U	R	T	J	R	Y	R	O	T	U	M	D	E	W	V	D	R	R
R	E	O	K	C	U	W	B	T	K	E	D	O	W	E	C	C	G
E	D	O	B	O	Y	N	R	R	G	N	P	N	R	I	R	L	Y
D	N	F	N	A	T	M	D	A	U	R	L	S	J	H	N	L	T
N	U	R	X	T	Y	A	R	E	E	S	H	T	L	C	F	E	U
U	L	E	Q	T	C	E	E	D	R	I	H	K	K	A	N	S	N
N	V	D	K	H	D	Z	N	R	R	P	D	D	H	R	N	R	D
N	R	N	H	N	B	U	X	T	E	L	A	B	R	E	T	E	E
K	F	U	U	M	R	P	F	K	T	D	J	S	M	D	N	D	R
Q	U	N	D	E	R	W	O	R	L	D	N	N	S	N	T	N	P
N	Z	R	D	E	Z	I	S	R	E	D	N	U	T	U	H	U	A
N	D	X	E	N	O	D	R	E	D	N	U	J	V	C	W	L	Y

underachieve	undereat	undersell
underaged	underfoot	undershirt
underarm	underlap	undersized
underbrush	underline	undertaker
undercoat	underpass	undertow
undercut	underpay	underused
underdone	underpowered	underworld

LOOK OUT BELOW!

Fill in the blanks using the words at the bottom of the page that all mean "below or not enough of something."

Why do they mean below or not enough of something? ______________________

1. Pluto, who lived beneath the earth, was king of the ______________.
2. All of the order forms would not fit in the ______________ envelope.
3. When she received her check, Jenn felt very ______________ for all her work.
4. The baked potato that I ordered was hard and ______________.
5. My little brother cannot go to the Teen Center because he is ______________.
6. Sam was almost pulled out into the ocean by the strong ______________.
7. We got to the beach by driving through the ______________beneath the bay.
8. You should either ______________ or italicize titles of books.
9. Clearing out the ______________ in the woods helps prevent fires.
10. Max is an ______________. He could make much better grades than he does.

Check off these words as you use them.

underachiever	underage	underbrush	underdone	underline
underpaid	underpass	undersized	undertow	underworld

PREFIX SQUARE

for **out**- meaning "beyond or more than"

Start in the middle square with the prefix **out** and combine this part with the words in the other squares to build new words. Write each word and a definition you can think of for it in the spaces provided at the bottom of the page.

rank	weigh	run
stretched	**out-**	grow
play	roar	spoken

AFFIX ADDER

The prefix out- means "beyond or more than."

1. Write **out** in the blank space in front of each word listed below and make a new word.
2. Tell what you think the new word means.
3. Write a sentence using the new word.

We've done one for you:

SCORE means to make points

...so OUTSCORE means to make more points than.

Sentence: If you want to win the game, you have to outscore the other team!

1. LAST means to continue or survive

...so ______LAST means ______

Used in a sentence:

2. POUR means to make flow

...so ______POUR means ______

Used in a sentence:

3. CAST means to send away

...so ______CAST means ______

Used in a sentence:

4. BID means to make an offer to buy

...so ______BID means ______

Used in a sentence:

5. WORK means to put forth effort

...so ______WORK means ________________________________

Used in a sentence:

6. PRODUCE means to make

...so ______PRODUCE means ________________________________

Used in a sentence:

7. DID means performed or accomplished

...so ______DID means ________________________________

Used in a sentence:

8. LAW means rule of society

...so ______LAW means ________________________________

Used in a sentence:

9. BURST means to fly apart suddenly

...so ______ BURST means ________________________________

Used in a sentence:

10. NUMBER means to add up to

...so ______ NUMBER means ________________________________

Used in a sentence:

MAGIC SQUARE

for **out**- meaning "beyond or more than"

Select the best definition for each of the words in the **out** family. Put the number of the definition in the proper space in the Magic Square box. If the numbers going up and down and the numbers going across all add up to the same thing, you have found the magic number!

WORDS

A. outlook
B. outfield
C. outdated
D. outline
E. outpost
F. outreach
G. outlive
H. outscore
I. outdistance

DEFINITIONS

1. to see from above
2. old fashioned; beyond modern time
3. to earn more points than those of an opponent
4. the shape of a thing
5. to be alive beyond the death of another person or animal
6. to stretch beyond a limit
7. the baseball field playing area beyond the diamond
8. a fort beyond a settlement
9. the view beyond the present time
10. to go farther or beyond another

Magic Square Box

A.	B.	C.
D.	E.	F.
G.	H.	I.

Magic Number ______

Name ____________________________

WORD SEARCH

Words with the suffix out- meaning beyond or more than

Find and circle the words in the grid. Words can go across or up and down, straight of diagonally, forwards or backwards.

```
H O X T M Q M J L L O U T S P R E A D
Z U T N E I T A P T U O H M H B T R Y
L T G F F Q M L N R V M N K B R X M L
N S M Z D P T O N T G O T S A C T U O
R M K W P C U W S E U W H J L P D F V
N A F K W T K A R T J D C P B K E L K
I R C W P P O Q B A W H A M C R H F Y
A T O O K B K R D D P K E X M M C Y N
G E S U T O E Q J T K F R X R K T O O
R T M U T A U N J U O U T L I V E U U
A M O O K G K T N O K F U D T M R T T
B R G X C V R E S N K R O S Y D T L S
T T F N Q T K O J C Y F R T B R S O O
U L X R I O U X W H O O K L R N T O U
O H K R P O F O H T O R P T B W U K R
D L M S J W G Q Z D H J E N X K O R C
L Q T L P L Q T T Y O U T F I E L D E
X U F B N N N U U L R B K P G C H T G
O D H V Q C O Q B O K M C N P K W M D
```

outbargain	outfield	outreach
outboast	outgoing	outscore
outbreak	outgrowth	outsmart
outcast	outlive	outsource
outcome	outlook	outspoken
outdate	outpatient	outspread
outdoors	outpost	outstretched

IT'S BEYOND ME!

Fill in the blanks using the words at the bottom of the page that all mean "beyond or more than."

Why do they mean beyond or more than? ______________________________

1. Ninety percent of all animals are insects. Insects ________________ all the other animals 9 to 1.
2. The bright planet Venus ________________ everything in the sky except the sun and moon.
3. The old couple Baucis and Philemon wanted to die at the same time; neither wanted to ________________ the other.
4. Jamahl ________________ us, so he won the debate.
5. Which brand of cereal do you think ________________ all others?
6. The clever fox would nearly always ______________ the other animals in the fables.
7. The long-distance runner had ________________ six pairs of shoes in a year.
8. In one story the slow turtle actually ________________ the quick hare.
9. In the surrounding ________________ of the city you can find orchards and cowfields.
10. Aunt Eleanor happily ran toward her nephew with ________________ arms.

Check off these words as you use them.

outargued	outran	outshines	outsmart	outstretched
outnumber	outsell	outskirts	outlive	outworn

SUFFIX SQUARE

for -**s** meaning "he, she, or it does"

Start in the middle square with the suffix **s** and combine this part with the words in the other squares to build new words. Write each word and a definition you can think of for it in the spaces provided at the bottom of the page.

talk	work	care
dance	-s	control
fit	love	mail

____

____

____

____

____

____

____

____

AFFIX ADDER

The suffix -s added to a verb makes the verb mean "he, she, or it does" (whatever is the action of the verb).

1. Write **s** in the blank space after each word listed below and make a new word.
2. Tell what you think the new word means.
3. Write a sentence using the new word.

We've done one for you:

READ means to get information from words and symbols
...so READS means he or she gets information from words and symbols.
Sentence: He reads to find things out, and she reads for pleasure.

---

1. CLEAN means to make free of soil
...so CLEAN___ means ______________________________
Used in a sentence:

____

2. COOK means make suitable for eating by applying heat
...so COOK___ means ______________________________
Used in a sentence:

____

3. EMPLOY means to put to use
...so EMPLOY___ means ______________________________
Used in a sentence:

____

4. FORM means to shape
...so FORM___ means ______________________________
Used in a sentence:

____

5. HEAT means to warm

...so HEAT____ means ____

Used in a sentence:

6. HOOK means to fasten

...so HOOK____ means ____

Used in a sentence:

7. PAINT means to apply a coating to

...so PAINT____ means ____

Used in a sentence:

8. TEST means to check on

...so TEST____ means ____

Used in a sentence:

9. TRUST means to believe or have faith in

...so TRUST____ means ____

Used in a sentence:

10. STAY means to remain

...so STAY____ means ____

Used in a sentence:

MAGIC SQUARE

for -**s** meaning "he, she, or it does (the action of the verb)"

Select the best definition for each of the words in the **s** family. Put the number of the definition in the proper space in the Magic Square box. If the numbers going up and down and the numbers going across all add up to the same thing, you have found the magic number!

WORDS

A. runs
B. stays
C. talks
D. crates
E. vacations
F. grades
G. rolls
H. hooks
I. bakes

DEFINITIONS

1. puts dressing on a salad
2. says words
3. fastens with a curved item
4. puts into boxes for storing or shipping
5. turns over and over
6. scores a paper or test
7. remains in the same place
8. takes a trip or time off for rest and relaxation
9. goes faster than a walk
10. cooks with dry heat

Magic Square Box

A.	B.	C.
D.	E.	F.
G.	H.	I.

Magic Number ______

Name ____________________

WORD SEARCH

Words with suffix -s, meaning "he, she, or it does"

Find and circle all the words in the grid. Words can go across or up and down, straight or diagonally, forwards or backwards.

Y	I	N	J	U	R	E	S	C	Q	M	D	Z	Y
D	B	R	F	Q	P	W	S	S	R	A	E	H	Y
Y	F	F	S	W	L	S	S	E	M	K	N	R	C
P	K	H	A	T	Y	D	S	R	G	T	B	T	O
K	L	L	R	A	A	K	B	U	E	D	V	H	N
T	K	T	L	E	C	E	S	B	N	N	U	K	N
S	S	P	R	A	F	D	E	X	R	I	T	J	E
E	E	A	P	Z	F	N	L	S	N	T	T	S	C
G	V	T	T	N	D	Y	B	K	Z	X	R	E	T
N	E	T	M	S	T	M	M	C	W	R	A	P	S
A	I	E	R	O	P	X	A	O	S	N	U	R	J
R	L	N	V	M	V	G	R	L	G	Q	K	M	Y
R	E	D	N	K	M	E	C	N	J	G	B	T	G
A	B	S	B	K	R	W	S	B	U	Y	S	T	R

arranges	hears	reads
attends	injures	rents
believes	judges	runs
bends	locks	scrambles
buys	moves	unites
connects	packs	walks
eats	plays	wraps

Just Do It!

Fill in the blanks using the words below that all mean "he, she or it does something."

Why do they mean he, she or it does something? ______________________________

1. As soon as Miss Johnson _______________ the test, I'll know how I did.
2. Jameel _______________ so fast I'm afraid he will get a stomach ache.
3. Marika _______________ so much I don't get a chance to say anything.
4. The soccer team _______________ really hard to get ready to play.
5. My mom _______________ pasta just the way I like it.
6. Once Joe _______________ the battery, we hope the car will start.
7. Carter _______________ her hat to her belt so it won't blow away.
8. My dog _______________ when I tell him to so he won't follow us.
9. Jacoby _______________ Caroline, but she doesn't feel the same way about him.
10. If the dress _______________ Melissa, she is going to buy it.

Check off these words as you use them.

talks	hooks	stays	eats	loves
practices	recharges	grades	fits	cooks

SUFFIX SQUARE

for -**er** meaning "more"

Start in the middle square with the suffix **er** and combine this part with the words in the other squares to build new words. Write each word and a definition you can think of for it in the spaces provided at the bottom of the page.

short	thick	quick
small	**-er**	soon
bright	soft	hard

____

____

____

____

____

____

____

____

AFFIX ADDER

The suffix -**er** means "more."

1. Write **er** in the blank space after each word listed below and make a new word.
2. Tell what you think the new word means.
3. Write a sentence using the new word.

We've done one for you:

RICH means having wealth
...so RICHER means having more wealth.

Sentence: America is richer than any other country in the world.

---

1. LOUD means high in volume
...so LOUD ____ means ______________________________
Used in a sentence:

---

2. SWEET means pleasing; like the taste of sugar
...so SWEET ____ means ______________________________
Used in a sentence:

---

3. STRONG means powerful
...so STRONG ____ means ______________________________
Used in a sentence:

---

4. CALM means peaceful
...so CALM ____ means ______________________________
Used in a sentence:

---

5. DEEP means far down below the surface

...so DEEP ___ means ______________________

Used in a sentence:

6. FEW means small in number

...so FEW___ means ______________________

Used in a sentence:

7. HIGH means far above the surface

...so HIGH ___ means ______________________

Used in a sentence:

8. LONG means stretched out

...so LONG ___ means ______________________

Used in a sentence:

9. LOW means slightly above the surface

...so LOW___ means ______________________

Used in a sentence:

10. MEEK means humble and gentle

...so MEEK ___ means ______________________

Used in a sentence:

MAGIC SQUARE

for -**er** meaning "more"

Select the best definition for each of the words in the **er** family. Put the number of the definition in the proper space in the Magic Square box. If the numbers going up and down and the numbers going across all add up to the same thing, you have found the magic number!

WORDS

A. colder
B. greener
C. cleaner
D. lighter
E. smoother
F. smarter
G. older
H. rougher
I. faster

DEFINITIONS

1. more small
2. more free of dirt
3. more harsh or having more bumps
4. more visible or shiny
5. having more years of age
6. knowing or understanding more
7. having more plants
8. not as harsh or bumpy
9. more like ice or snow
10. more speedy

Magic Square Box

A.	B.	C.
D.	E.	F.
G.	H.	I.

Magic Number ______

Name ______________________

WORD SEARCH

Words with the suffix -er, meaning "more."

Find and circle the words in the grid. Words can go across or up and down, straight or diagonally, forwards or backwards.

F	T	F	W	F	I	R	M	E	R	R	D	R	M
K	R	E	P	M	A	D	T	P	E	Z	E	M	O
L	R	E	D	L	O	B	L	W	N	T	I	L	I
D	F	R	F	A	S	T	E	R	R	L	X	Q	S
R	U	O	E	V	Q	N	T	O	D	M	Z	R	T
E	M	M	N	D	Q	B	H	E	R	M	R	T	E
G	C	D	B	D	R	S	R	R	C	M	E	Q	R
N	L	F	Y	E	E	A	K	S	H	D	H	R	D
O	E	M	N	D	R	R	H	R	T	R	G	E	U
L	A	N	M	S	M	A	R	T	E	R	I	D	L
H	R	V	W	C	R	Q	Z	W	Z	K	H	L	L
M	E	D	P	P	C	B	O	Q	M	L	N	O	E
X	R	N	E	X	Y	L	R	M	Y	D	Z	I	R
L	B	R	I	G	H	T	E	R	L	L	W	H	P

bolder	firmer	moister
brighter	fonder	newer
clearer	harder	older
damper	higher	pinker
duller	longer	sharper
dumber	lower	shorter
faster	milder	smarter

Give me MORE

Fill in the blanks using the words below that all mean "more."
Why do they mean more? ___________________________

1. If these lights were any ______________ they would blind me!
2. Maria can run ______________ that Charlotte.
3. James is ______________ than Anna, so he can fit in the back seat.
4. Gunston is ______________ than I am, so he lost his wisdom teeth first.
5. Jalepeño peppers are ______________ than green peppers.
6. The peak of Mt. Everest is ____________ than any other place on earth.
7. The days are ____________ in the wintertime than in the summertime.
8. A feather is _____________ than a rock.
9. The days are ____________ in the summertime than in the wintertime.
10. It is always _____________ at the North Pole than it is in Mexico.

<u>Check off these words as you use them</u>

smaller	shorter	brighter	colder	softer
faster	older	longer	hotter	higher

SUFFIX SQUARE

for -**est** meaning "most"

Start in the middle square with the suffix **est** and combine this part with the words in the other squares to build new words. Write each word and a definition you can think of for it in the spaces provided at the bottom of the page.

kind	poor	tender
neat	-**est**	fast
straight	cheap	clear

AFFIX ADDER

The suffix -est means "most."

1. Write **est** in the blank space after each word listed below and make a new word.
2. Tell what you think the new word means.
3. Write a sentence using the new word.

We've done one for you:

CLEAR means plain to see or easy to understand
...so CLEAR<u>EST</u> means <u>most plain to see or most easy to understand.</u>
<u>Sentence</u>: I need the clearest instructions I can get to find your house.

1. BOLD means fearless and daring
...so BOLD ____ means ______________________________
<u>Used in a sentence</u>:

2. DAMP means moist
...so DAMP ____ means ______________________________
<u>Used in a sentence</u>:

3. DEAR means valuable; loved and cherished
...so DEAR ____ means ______________________________
<u>Used in a sentence</u>:

4. FIRM means solid
...so FiRM____ means ______________________________
<u>Used in a sentence</u>:

5. GRAND means large and impressive
...so GRAND___ means ______________________________
Used in a sentence:

6. KIND means nice and friendly
...so KIND___ means ______________________________
Used in a sentence:

7. MEAN means inconsiderate and unfriendly
...so MEAN ___ means ______________________________
Used in a sentence:

8. NEW means fresh and recently made
...so NEW___ means ______________________________
Used in a sentence:

9. PROUD means feeling great satisfaction
...so PROUD___ means ______________________________
Used in a sentence:

10. WEAK means lacking power
...so WEAK___ means ______________________________
Used in a sentence:

MAGIC SQUARE

for -**est** meaning "most"

Select the best definition for each of the words in the **est** family. Put the number of the definition in the proper space in the Magic Square box. If the numbers going up and down and the numbers going across all add up to the same thing, you have found the magic number!

WORDS

A. freshest
B. sharpest
C. cruelest
D. fairest
E. proudest
F. faintest
G. swiftest
H. briefest
I. steepest

DEFINITIONS

1. being the most near
2. having the most newness
3. having the most incline or slope
4. having the most good feeling for what is done
5. lasting the most shortness of time
6. being the most nice and right
7. being the most nasty and evil
8. being the most difficult to see or hear
9. having the most pointed end
10. being the most fast

Magic Square Box

A.	B.	C.
D.	E.	F.
G.	H.	I.

Magic Number ______

Name ____________________

WORD SEARCH

Words with suffix -est, meaning "most."

Find and circle all the words in the grid. Words can go across or up and down, straight or diagonally, forwards or backwards.

T	T	S	E	T	N	I	A	F	C	M	T	T	M	J	J
T	L	M	G	N	S	O	U	R	E	S	T	V	B	T	T
S	Z	B	B	I	T	T	E	R	E	S	T	G	S	L	L
E	K	M	R	B	D	B	V	K	R	C	B	E	W	C	P
T	T	M	M	I	N	R	E	P	H	O	G	H	E	B	M
H	Z	E	K	Z	E	E	R	E	L	N	Z	T	A	B	X
G	L	G	N	N	M	F	A	D	U	N	S	B	K	T	K
I	T	N	L	D	T	P	E	O	Y	E	K	R	E	N	V
A	V	S	N	C	E	S	Y	S	K	T	B	O	S	T	C
R	Z	T	E	S	T	R	E	E	T	S	K	A	T	S	L
T	Y	V	T	D	R	L	E	D	M	E	X	D	H	E	E
S	L	L	M	C	U	L	V	S	N	T	N	E	W	S	A
C	N	V	C	N	S	O	L	W	T	A	Q	S	D	S	R
Y	T	S	E	H	S	E	R	F	B	E	R	T	N	O	E
P	L	A	I	N	E	S	T	P	P	R	C	G	M	R	S
N	T	T	S	E	P	E	E	T	S	G	N	M	T	G	T

bitterest	freshest	sleekest
boldest	grandest	sourest
briefest	greatest	steepest
broadest	grossest	straightest
cheapest	meekest	tenderest
clearest	plainest	weakest
faintest	proudest	youngest

Only the BEST!

Fill in the blanks using the words below that all mean "most."
Why do they mean <u>most</u>? ______________________________

1. I buy things on sale when they are _____________.
2. In 2006, Phil Pfister was the world's _____________man. He lifted 5 weights totaling 2,750 pounds in a world record time of 31.92 seconds!
3. The _____________vegetables are found at the farmer's market.
4. The world's _____________ ball of string can be found in Cawker, Kansas.
5. Dad tells the _____________ stories. They put me to sleep!
6. Mt. Everest is the _____________ mountain on earth.
7. The world's _____________living man (8'4") is Radhouane Charbib of Tunisia.
8. The _____________ person in a group is always the first to offer help.
9. The _____________ person in the world is Marilyn vos Savant, with an IQ of 228!
10. Hydrogen is the _____________ element, with an atomic weight of 1.

<u>Check off these words as you use them</u>.

freshest	highest	kindest	strongest	lightest
tallest	cheapest	smartest	longest	largest

SUFFIX SQUARE

for **-ed** meaning "did before now, in the past"

Start in the middle square with the suffix **ed** and combine this part with the words in the other squares to build new words. Write each word and a definition you can think of for it in the spaces provided at the bottom of the page.

ask	mark	want
rent	**-ed**	pick
answer	fear	invent

AFFIX ADDER

The suffix -ed means "did before now, in the past."

1. Write **ed** in the blank space after each word listed below and make a new word.
2. Tell what you think the new word means.
3. Write a sentence using the new word.

We've done one for you:

WALK means to move with steps slower than a run
...so WALKED means moved with steps slower than a run.

Sentence: I walked all the way to school this morning.

---

1. CLEAN means to make free of dirt
...so CLEAN___ means ______________________________
Used in a sentence:

---

2. COOK means to prepare and heat for eating
...so COOK___ means ______________________________
Used in a sentence:

---

3. EMPLOY means to put to use
...so EMPLOY___ means ______________________________
Used in a sentence:

---

4. FORM means to shape
...so FORM___ means ______________________________
Used in a sentence:

---

5. HEAT means to warm

...so HEAT___ means ______________________

Used in a sentence:

____

6. HOOK means to fasten

...so HOOK___ means ______________________

Used in a sentence:

____

7. PAINT means to apply a coating to

...so PAINT___ means ______________________

Used in a sentence:

____

8. TEST means to check on

...so TEST___ means ______________________

Used in a sentence:

____

9. TRUST means to believe or have faith in

...so TRUST___ means ______________________

Used in a sentence:

____

10. WASH means to clean with soap and water

...so WASH___ means ______________________

Used in a sentence:

____

MAGIC SQUARE

for -**ed** meaning "did before now, in the past"

Select the best definition for each of the words in the **ed** family. Put the number of the definition in the proper space in the Magic Square box. If the numbers going up and down and the numbers going across all add up to the same thing, you have found the magic number!

WORDS

A. enjoyed
B. finished
C. jumped
D. shouted
E. reached
F. started
G. returned
H. trained
I. wished

DEFINITIONS

1. spoke to
2. hopped up
3. taught to do something
4. spoke loudly
5. brought back or came back
6. began
7. got to the end
8. arrived at
9. took pleasure in
10. longed for or wanted

Magic Square Box

A.	B.	C.
D.	E.	F.
G.	H.	I.

Magic Number ______

Name ______________________

WORD SEARCH

Words with suffix -ed, meaning "did before now or in the past"

Find and circle all the words in the grid. Words can go across or up and down, straight or diagonally, forwards or backwards

D	K	J	U	M	P	E	D	B	Z	K	D	H	L	D	W	Y
E	L	W	T	Z	Y	K	F	J	Y	L	E	Y	R	L	Y	M
T	G	F	P	P	J	L	M	R	R	Q	T	M	B	C	N	J
S	Y	D	E	T	N	E	V	N	I	D	C	D	M	Q	G	B
E	D	B	Y	K	T	R	R	T	E	Z	E	C	V	K	N	P
G	D	W	W	K	Q	K	K	H	B	T	N	R	P	R	B	R
G	P	E	R	C	N	B	S	Q	N	W	N	Y	V	L	E	B
U	A	R	T	H	D	I	T	E	K	D	O	H	N	A	R	D
S	R	P	N	U	N	D	S	F	E	N	C	N	C	B	C	D
W	K	W	C	I	O	E	E	R	H	F	G	H	Y	M	R	E
I	E	L	F	O	R	H	A	K	I	S	E	O	X	G	O	K
S	D	R	X	P	V	E	S	S	O	D	T	T	W	T	S	C
H	T	N	X	C	P	E	H	L	P	O	T	A	L	N	S	I
E	B	C	H	P	M	E	R	N	M	Q	L	J	Y	V	E	P
D	K	G	A	R	D	B	H	E	P	T	B	R	V	E	D	D
D	E	N	R	U	T	E	R	J	D	P	U	S	H	E	D	T
T	C	P	H	V	W	W	M	E	N	J	O	Y	E	D	C	M

appeared	invented	pushed
connected	jumped	reached
covered	looked	returned
crossed	owned	shouted
enjoyed	parked	stayed
finished	picked	suggested
fished	presented	wished

You did it!

Fill in the blanks using the words below that all mean "did before now, in the past."

Why do they mean did before now, in the past? ______________________________

1. I ______________ my money to see if I had enough.
2. My dad ______________ the house because the old paint was cracking.
3. Thomas Edison ______________ the light bulb.
4. Kate didn't answer the phone, so I used my computer and ______________ her.
5. I ______________ Joe on the phone to remind him about the game.
6. My iPod broke, so I took it to the repair shop and they ______________ it.
7. Mary ______________ 10 copies of her report.
8. My father ______________ to take me to the park instead of mowing the lawn.
9. Suzanne ______________ like she didn't know Juan, but she did.
10. John ______________ while on vacation and caught a big one!

Check off these words as you use them.

painted	invented	counted	fixed	fished
printed	acted	called	emailed	wanted

PREFIX SQUARE

for **un-** meaning "not, or opposite of"

Start in the middle square with the prefix **un** and combine this part with the words in the other squares to build new words. Write each word and a definition you can think of for it in the spaces provided at the bottom of the page.

claimed	believable	arranged
changing	**un-**	clean
considered	comfortable	afraid

AFFIX ADDER

The prefix un- means "not, or opposite of."

1. Write **un** in the blank space in front of each word listed below and make a new word.
2. Tell what you think the new word means.
3. Write a sentence using the new word.

We've done one for you:

LOCK means to make secure

...so UNLOCK means the opposite of lock: to make not secure.

Sentence: I had to unlock my front door before going in with the groceries.

1. AWARE means mentally awake

   ...so ____ AWARE means ______________________________

   Used in a sentence:

2. CERTAIN means sure

   ...so ____ CERTAIN means ______________________________

   Used in a sentence:

3. COMMON means ordinary

   ...so ____ COMMON means ______________________________

   Used in a sentence:

4. NECESSARY means needed

   ...so ____ NECESSARY means ______________________________

   Used in a sentence:

5. EQUAL means even or the same

...so ____ EQUAL means ______________________________

Used in a sentence:

6. FORTUNATE means lucky

...so ____ FORTUNATE means ______________________________

Used in a sentence:

7. GRATEFUL means thankful

...so ____ GRATEFUL means ______________________________

Used in a sentence:

8. IMPORTANT means matters a lot

...so ____ IMPORTANT means ______________________________

Used in a sentence:

9. INVITED means welcomed

...so ____ INVITED means ______________________________

Used in a sentence:

10. JUST means fair and right

...so ____ JUST means ______________________________

Used in a sentence:

MAGIC SQUARE

for **un-** meaning "not, or opposite of"

Select the best definition for each of the words in the **un** family. Put the number of the definition in the proper space in the Magic Square box. If the numbers going up and down and the numbers going across all add up to the same thing, you have found the magic number!

WORDS

A. unbreakable
B. untried
C. uncooked
D. unfurnished
E. unlike
F. unseen
G. untruthful
H. unstable
I. unhappy

DEFINITIONS

1. not glad
2. not equipped
3. not tested or experienced
4. not the same
5. not heated for eating; raw
6. not honest or real
7. not able to be hurt or damaged
8. not firm or steady
9. not in view; hidden

Magic Square Box

A.	B.	C.
D.	E.	F.
G.	H.	I.

Magic Number ______

Name ______________________

Word Search

Words with prefix un- meaning "not; opposite of or absence of"

Find and circle all the words in the grid. Words can go across or up and down, straight or diagonally, forwards or backwards.

```
G V U U K X X T U N E M P L O Y E D M
H M N N L T E R X K E D M N M F M E F
L G N M F U Q L W L I T D B T K U K G
K N E I K Y N Q B A W E A Q Q N N O R
D Y I S G F Y B R A R U K E O G G O D
R X G T P K X F R E T U N P N Y L C E
J E H A T Y A C V E N R E L P U T N K
B L B K B N P O Y C A N O P I N C U C
M B O A U M C W L Q E K A F K K K W I
V A R B T N G E Z D Q H A U M T E R P
U T L L U V A N Z Q N B G B N O N D N
N P Y E M N Y R B U M J K Y L S C P U
C E W U N B E L I E V A B L E E O N N
L C P C N B U N N E C E S S A R Y L U
A C P L F T L U F H T U R T N U N K D
I A R A E L C N U H N R M M L R K K B
M N B V J H L Y L L E L B A S U N U N
E U F N F L V K V E L B A D A E R N U
D G U N F U R N I S H E D G G R X Z L
```

unacceptable	uncooked	unnecessary
unafraid	uncovered	unneighborly
unbelievable	uneaten	unopened
unbreakable	unemployed	unpicked
unclaimed	unfurnished	unreadable
unclean	unhappy	unsold
unclear	unlike	untruthful
uncomfortable	unmistakable	unusable

Not!

Fill in the blanks using the words below that all mean "not something".

Why do they mean not something? ______________________________

1. It is _____________ if you get 2 pieces of candy and I only get one.
2. It is hard to walk on a sidewalk that is ____________.
3. The banana was _____________ so I couldn't eat it yet.
4. The directions were hard to understand because they were _____________.
5. The __________________ guest was not welcome.
6. My friends were scared, but I was _______________ of the roller coaster.
7. Potatoes that are raw are ________________.
8. The ______________ kittens were still inside mama cat.
9. I dropped the tray and only one of the glasses was ___________________.
10. We had to wash the dirty dishes because they were ________________.

Check off these words as you use them.

unclear	uninvited	unfair	unripe	unclean
uneven	unafraid	uncooked	unbroken	unborn

SUFFIX SQUARE

for **-ing** meaning "going on, happening now"

Start in the middle square with the suffix **ing** and combine this part with the words in the other squares to build new words. Write each word and a definition you can think of for it in the spaces provided at the bottom of the page.

eat	work	go
try	**-ing**	pick
read	talk	sell

____

____

____

____

____

____

____

____

AFFIX ADDER

The suffix -ing means "going on, happening now."

1. Write **ing** in the blank space after each word listed below and make a new word.
2. Tell what you think the new word means.
3. Write a sentence using the new word.

We've done one for you:

WALK means to move with steps slower than a run
...so WALKING means moving with steps slower than a run.
Sentence: I am walking all the way to school this morning.

1. APPEAR means to come into view
...so APPEAR ____ means ______________________________
Used in a sentence:

2. BUILD means to make from parts
...so BUILD ____ means ______________________________
Used in a sentence:

3. COPY means to make another one of
...so COPY ____ means ______________________________
Used in a sentence:

4. FOLD means to double over
...so FOLD ____ means ______________________________
Used in a sentence:

5. HEAT means to warm

...so HEAT___ means ______________________________

Used in a sentence:

6. LOAD means to fill

...so LOAD___ means ______________________________

Used in a sentence:

7. MARRY means to take a husband or wife

...so MARRY___ means ______________________________

Used in a sentence:

8. OPEN means to take away the cover, lid, or cap

...so OPEN____ means ______________________________

Used in a sentence:

9. PAY means to give in return for goods or services

...so PAY____ means ______________________________

Used in a sentence:

10. VIEW means to look at

...so VIEW____ means ______________________________

Used in a sentence:

MAGIC SQUARE

for -**ing** meaning "going on, happening now"

Select the best definition for each of the words in the **ing** family. Put the number of the definition in the proper space in the Magic Square box. If the numbers going up and down and the numbers going across all add up to the same thing, you have found the magic number!

WORDS

A. comforting
B. agreeing
C. answering
D. failing
E. governing
F. lifting
G. crossing
H. guessing
I. inventing

DEFINITIONS

1. constructing again
2. responding to a question
3. randomly choosing answers
4. not passing or succeeding
5. traveling over
6. raising up
7. having the same opinion
8. ruling or guiding
9. making feel better
10. creating something new

Magic Square Box

A.	B.	C.
D.	E.	F.
G.	H.	I.

Magic Number ______

Name ______________________

WORD SEARCH

Words with suffix -ing, meaning "going on, happening now"

Find and circle all the words in the grid. Words can go across or up and down, straight or diagonally, forwards or backwards.

F	I	L	L	I	N	G	R	G	P	U	L	L	I	N	G
D	R	F	C	Y	G	L	F	O	N	W	J	L	G	B	B
C	L	B	R	F	G	N	J	R	C	I	Y	M	W	G	K
L	W	K	R	K	T	U	I	X	M	K	S	X	L	N	M
I	L	A	H	C	M	K	N	S	W	C	I	S	N	I	J
M	D	W	S	P	N	W	Z	J	S	X	W	N	O	K	F
B	N	F	I	H	C	L	E	A	N	I	N	G	G	R	T
I	L	N	I	W	I	G	D	C	K	R	M	N	N	A	C
N	G	M	Q	S	N	N	D	F	C	L	I	G	I	P	G
G	N	T	R	I	H	D	G	O	G	N	S	N	Y	Z	U
M	Y	B	S	Z	G	I	L	D	R	D	I	I	R	N	E
L	W	S	Q	N	C	O	N	U	M	K	G	W	C	T	S
C	A	N	I	Q	R	B	B	G	W	T	N	O	V	G	S
P	L	D	V	I	M	G	T	T	W	Z	I	L	M	L	I
V	N	B	N	G	N	I	D	N	A	L	N	B	K	J	N
E	P	G	L	G	N	I	K	O	O	C	G	Y	C	T	G

blowing	crying	missing
burning	ending	parking
cleaning	filling	passing
climbing	fishing	pulling
coloring	guessing	rocking
cooking	jumping	signing
crossing	landing	washing

Right Now!

Fill in the blanks using the words below that all mean "doing something right now."

Why do they mean doing something right now? ______________________________

1. Singers are always ________________ new ways to say "I love you."
2. Kate was ________________ a book and Jim kept bothering her.
3. ________________ a match near a gas station is a bad idea.
4. Joe can't play today because he and his dad are _______________ his room.
5. My bike has a flat tire, so I took it to the repair shop and they are ____________ it.
6. I am ______________ my report on really nice paper.
7. We are ______________ because my mom got a job in Cleveland.
8. The person in the play is ______________ like someone else.
9. Marika and Shawn are ______________ for trout.
10. Rondell is ________________ his money to see if he has enough.

Check off these words as you use them.

painting	inventing	counting	fixing	fishing
printing	acting	moving	reading	lighting

PREFIX SQUARE

for **re**- meaning "again, back, or against"

Start in the middle square with the prefix **re** and combine this part with the words in the other squares to build new words. Write each word and a definition you can think of for it in the spaces provided at the bottom of the page.

act	appear	arrange
build	**re**-	call
think	create	plant

AFFIX ADDER

The prefix re- means "again, back, or against."

1. Write **re** in the blank space in front of each word listed below and make a new word.
2. Tell what you think the new word means.
3. Write a sentence using the new word.

We've done one for you:

GROUP means to put together
...so REGROUP means to put together again.
Sentence: After their big loss, the team decided to regroup.

1. ARRANGE means to place in order
...so ____ ARRANGE means ______________________________
Used in a sentence:

2. FASTEN means to join together
...so ____ FASTEN means ______________________________
Used in a sentence:

3. FORM means to shape
...so ____ FORM means ______________________________
Used in a sentence:

4. HEAT means to warm
...so ____ HEAT means ______________________________
Used in a sentence:

5. OPEN means to take away the cover, lid, or cap
...so ____ OPEN means ______________________________

Used in a sentence:

____

6. PAINT means to apply a coating to
...so ____ PAINT means ______________________________

Used in a sentence:

____

7. PLACE means to put something
...so ____ PLACE means ______________________________

Used in a sentence:

____

8. STATE means to say
...so ____ STATE means ______________________________

Used in a sentence:

____

9. VIEW means to see
...so ____ VIEW means ______________________________

Used in a sentence:

____

10. WRITE means to put thoughts on paper
...so ____ WRITE means ______________________________

Used in a sentence:

____

MAGIC SQUARE

for **re**- meaning "again, back, or against"

Select the best definition for each of the words in the **re** family. Put the number of the definition in the proper space in the Magic Square box. If the numbers going up and down and the numbers going across all add up to the same thing, you have found the magic number!

WORDS

A. react
B. reappear
C. rearrange
D. rebuild
E. repay
F. reconnect
G. recall
H. reheat
I. reforest

DEFINITIONS

1. to plant trees again
2. to make or construct again
3. to come into view again
4. to give money back again
5. to straighten up again in a new way
6. to ask that a product be returned
7. to respond or move in return
8. to raise the temperature again
9. to attach or hook back together

Magic Square Box

A.	B.	C.
D.	E.	F.
G.	H.	I.

Magic Number ______

Name ________________________

WORD SEARCH

Words with prefix re- meaning "again, back, or against"

Find and circle all the words in the grid. Words can go across or up and down, straight or diagonally, forwards or backwards.

W	Z	K	Y	M	R	E	C	O	U	N	T	Q	R	W
R	R	R	E	T	N	E	E	R	G	Z	N	R	K	E
T	E	E	R	K	T	C	E	L	L	O	C	E	R	I
N	C	P	C	K	H	R	E	F	O	R	M	Y	X	V
R	N	E	L	O	L	H	P	B	P	Q	P	M	B	E
E	A	L	R	A	N	N	M	Y	U	K	O	T	K	R
F	R	E	H	I	N	S	E	M	O	B	L	Z	K	J
I	E	F	P	P	D	T	I	G	R	L	E	Y	H	R
N	C	Y	Y	P	A	E	R	D	G	K	V	S	R	E
I	O	Z	L	E	A	E	R	W	E	Q	E	K	M	R
S	N	D	R	J	C	E	E	X	R	R	D	L	H	E
H	N	C	W	A	F	N	R	J	F	G	E	R	X	A
K	E	F	L	I	E	X	L	E	L	M	R	Z	P	D
R	C	L	L	R	E	W	R	I	T	E	F	T	Y	R
Y	T	L	B	N	G	Y	B	D	L	I	U	B	E	R

reappear	recreate	refresh
rebuild	redevelop	regroup
recall	redirect	renew
recollect	reenter	replant
reconnect	refill	reread
reconsider	refinish	review
recount	reform	rewrite

ONE MORE TIME!

Fill in the blanks using the words below that all mean "to do something again."

Why do they mean to do something again? ______________________________

1. I used the toy a long time ago, so I had to _______________ the directions.
2. My dad had to _______________ the house because the old paint was cracking.
3. The candle blew out, so I had to _______________ it.
4. I forgot how many cards were in my pile, so I had to _______________ them.
5. The ink ran low when I printed my story, so I had to _______________ it.
6. My hot chocolate got cold, so I had to _____________ it.
7. The door blew shut, so I had to _____________ it.
8. I had to ______________ my fort because John knocked it down.
9. The teacher didn't like my story, so I had to _______________ it.
10. My computer crashed, so I had to ______________ it.

Check off these words as you use them.

relight	reopen	repaint	reread	restart
recount	reprint	rebuild	rewrite	reheat

SUFFIX SQUARE

for **-able** meaning "capable of, fit for, or worthy of"

Start in the middle square with the suffix **able** and combine this part with the words in the other squares to build new words. Write each word and a definition you can think of for it in the spaces provided at the bottom of the page.

laugh	depend	test
comfort	**-able**	agree
read	teach	present

AFFIX ADDER

The suffix -able means "capable of, fit for, or worthy of."

1. Write **able** in the blank space after each word listed below and make a new word.
2. Tell what you think the new word means.
3. Write a sentence using the new word.

We've done one for you:

COMFORT means to soothe
...so COMFORTABLE means capable of soothing.
Sentence: The easy chair I sit in is very comfortable.

1. ACCEPT means to take
...so ACCEPT_____ means ______________________________
Used in a sentence:

2. AGREE means to hold the same opinion
...so AGREE_____ means ______________________________
Used in a sentence:

3. BREAK means to split or smash into parts
...so BREAK_____ means ______________________________
Used in a sentence:

4. COLLECT means to gather together in a group
...so COLLECT_____ means ______________________________
Used in a sentence:

5. FAVOR means to show approval

...so FAVOR_____ means ____

Used in a sentence:

6. HONOR means to hold in respect

...so HONOR_____ means ____

Used in a sentence:

7. PREFER means to favor or choose one thing over another

...so PREFER_____ means ____

Used in a sentence:

8. RETURN means to bring back

...so RETURN_____ means ____

Used in a sentence:

9. WASH means to clean in water

...so WASH_____ means ____

Used in a sentence:

10. WORK means labor to move or do something

...so WORK_____ means ____

Used in a sentence:

MAGIC SQUARE

for -**able** meaning "capable of, fit for, or worthy of"

Select the best definition for each of the words in the **able** family. Put the number of the definition in the proper space in the Magic Square box. If the numbers going up and down and the numbers going across all add up to the same thing, you have found the magic number!

WORDS

A. paintable
B. allowable
C. buildable
D. passable
E. laughable
F. countable
G. affordable
H. printable
I. avoidable

DEFINITIONS

1. worthy of staying away from
2. worthy of being made fun of; humorous
3. ready for a new coat to be brushed on
4. fit for crossing over; worthy of a good grade
5. capable of being constructed
6. worthy to appear in a newspaper
7. worth letting happen
8. capable of being paid for
9. capable of being added up

Magic Square Box

A.	B.	C.
D.	E.	F.
G.	H.	I.

Magic Number ______

Name ______________________

WORD SEARCH

Words with suffix -able, meaning "capable of, fit for, or worthy of"

Find and circle all the words in the grid. Words can go across or up and down, straight or diagonally, forwards or backwards.

Y	C	X	J	W	L	D	H	Y	L	W	V	B	L	T	W	R	N
R	F	K	E	H	N	H	O	N	L	Y	T	D	R	E	D	K	E
H	L	R	L	K	N	L	N	F	V	P	K	T	A	H	K	X	L
X	A	M	B	E	Z	F	O	F	A	V	O	R	A	B	L	E	B
D	U	Z	A	L	D	N	R	E	L	B	A	H	C	A	E	T	A
R	G	X	N	B	L	M	A	Q	L	B	K	E	R	E	L	E	T
I	H	R	O	A	H	X	B	M	L	B	L	C	L	V	L	W	N
V	A	B	S	R	R	F	L	E	V	B	A	B	L	B	R	A	U
E	B	T	A	E	P	E	E	R	A	E	A	N	A	K	F	F	O
A	L	H	E	W	L	R	S	K	E	D	L	T	R	F	M	G	C
B	E	N	R	S	L	X	R	P	A	N	I	B	O	U	H	D	L
L	F	J	C	N	G	O	X	E	E	U	E	R	A	X	T	L	H
E	Z	T	N	A	W	N	R	Y	S	C	D	W	W	H	N	E	T
P	B	U	I	L	D	A	B	L	E	A	T	N	A	B	S	K	R
C	K	M	W	A	T	C	H	A	B	L	E	A	P	B	G	A	M
T	Y	B	N	C	F	K	K	L	B	B	Y	T	B	P	L	N	W
T	L	N	E	L	B	A	E	C	I	V	R	E	S	L	V	E	F
B	C	V	N	Y	Y	H	G	E	L	B	A	R	E	F	E	R	P

affordable	laughable	serviceable
answerable	preferable	suitable
buildable	readable	teachable
countable	reasonable	washable
driveable	renewable	watchable
favorable	respectable	wearable
honorable	returnable	workable

Fit as a Fiddle

Fill in the blanks using the words below that all mean "capable of, fit for, or worthy of." Why do they mean capable of, fit for, or worthy of? ______________________________

1. A good joke is ______________.
2. Print has to be large to be ______________ by me because my eyesight is poor.
3. Now that you have sanded the old table, it is ______________.
4. Soft chairs are very ______________.
5. Because I am a good learner, I am described as ______________.
6. A small pile of cards is ______________. A room full of cards is not.
7. With good instructions, even something with a lot of pieces is ______________.
8. Even a large mountain is ______________ if it isn't too steep.
9. Music needs a good beat to be ______________.
10. If something is broken but can be fixed, it is ______________.

Check off these words as you use them.

paintable	climbable	danceable	comfortable	readable
countable	laughable	teachable	buildable	repairable

PREFIX/SUFFIX SQUARE

for **un**- meaning "not, or opposite of"

plus -**able**, meaning "capable of, fit for, or worthy of"

Start in the middle square with the prefix **un** and the suffix **able** and combine both of these parts with the words in the other squares to build new words. Write each new word and the definition you can think of for it in the spaces provided at the bottom of the page.

accept	bend	elect
work	**un-** + **-able**	match
present	drink	afford

AFFIX ADDER

The prefix **un-** means "not, or opposite of."

The suffix **–able** means "capable of, fit for, or worthy of."

1. Write **un** in the blank space in front of each word and **able** in the blank space after each word listed below and make a new word.
2. Tell what you think the new word means.
3. Write a sentence using the new word.

We've done one for you:

BREAK means to split apart or smash into pieces

...so UNBREAKABLE means not capable of being smashed into pieces.

Sentence: These plastic dinner plates are unbreakable.

1. AGREE means to hold the same opinion
   ...so ____ AGREE ______ means ______________________________

   Used in a sentence:

2. FOLD means to double over
   ...so ____ FOLD______ means ______________________________

   Used in a sentence:

3. OPEN means to take the cover off
   ...so ____OPEN______ means ______________________________

   Used in a sentence:

4. READ means to view and understand written words
   ...so ____ READ______ means ______________________________

   Used in a sentence:

5. TRUST means to believe or have faith in
...so ____ TRUST______ means ________________________________
Used in a sentence:

6. WASH means to clean in water
...so ____ WASH______ means ________________________________
Used in a sentence:

7. BLOCK means to get in the way of
...so ____ BLOCK______ means ________________________________
Used in a sentence:

8. BUILD means to make from parts
...so ____ BUILD______ means ________________________________
Used in a sentence:

9. BEND means to change the shape of
...so ____ BEND______ means ________________________________
Used in a sentence:

10. ADJUST means to change so as to fit or correspond
...so ____ ADJUST______ means________________________________
Used in a sentence:

MAGIC SQUARE

for **un**- meaning "not, or opposite of"

plus -**able** meaning "capable of, fit for, or worthy of"

Select the best definition for each of the words in the **un** plus **able** family. Put the number of the definition in the proper space in the Magic Square box. If the numbers going up and down and the numbers going across all add up to the same thing, you have found the magic number!

WORDS

A. unaffordable
B. unpronounceable
C. unanswerable
D. unprofitable
E. unapproachable
F. unmanageable
G. unavoidable
H. unbreakable
I. unreturnable

DEFINITIONS

1. not able to be glued on
2. not worth giving a response to
3. not capable of being smashed
4. not capable of making extra money on
5. not capable of staying out of the way of
6. not capable of being handled or tamed
7. not capable of being said correctly
8. not fit for getting near to
9. not capable of being paid for
10. not able to be taken back

Magic Square Box

A.	B.	C.
D.	E.	F.
G.	H.	I.

Magic Number ______

Name ______________________

WORD SEARCH

Words with prefix un- meaning "not, or opposite of", and the suffix -able, meaning "capable of, fit for, or worthy of"

Find and circle all the words in the grid. Words can go across or up and down, straight or diagonally, forwards or backwards.

```
B B M B E L B A E G N A H C N U K R Z T E L
P F C G L L M L B K N E M K C E U R N V L T
M D T E K C L M Z H L U R H L B N N G N B T
U T E K L W K L P B T T N B K W B M R Z A V
R N T L K B G P A N Q F A F H F U Y D J M E
P M F L B K A D G L X N L G O E I K Z N I L
F E Y I P A A T R W E W J U L L L U P L A B
F L R G L E K D N T P T N B E K D N K K L A
R B X J R L G C S U Q C A M L D A A N X C N
E A B N B N A A O W O T R Y B B B D B F N O
L R U L P L F B L L N C R Q A M L J Y L U I
B E P Y T N L V L I B M N V H R E U U V E T
A W H G U M W E R E K N P U C Z C S N B U N
K S B T V L C P Z X L R U P U X Q T F L N E
A N L Z W T N G L C R B L T O V M A I B O M
E A R M A U F Y V L K W Y Q T N K B X R P N
R N H B R K R V L K Y Q D R N K M L A G E U
B U L K Y N D R T W K Q M F U H V E B W N Z
N E Z C N J K R T C L L D K K T W K L V A V
U L H P K M T L U N P L A C E A B L E M B L
U N A G R E E A B L E R P X Z Y X Z J G L L
D Q X C B H J K E L B A T P E C C A N U E Q
```

unacceptable	unchangeable	unfoldable
unadjustable	unclaimable	unmentionable
unagreeable	uncollectable	unopenable
unanswerable	uncountable	unplaceable
unblockable	unfastenable	unprintable
unbreakable	unfillable	unreadable
unbuildable	unfixable	untouchable

We're not Worthy....

Fill in the blanks using the words below that all mean "not capable of, not fit for, or not worthy of." Why do they mean not capable of, not fit for, or not worthy of?

____

1. A bad joke is ________________.
2. If print is too small it is ________________by me because my eyesight is poor.
3. Until you sand the old table, the surface is ________________.
4. Lumpy chairs are very ________________.
5. Because I never pay attention in school, I am described as ________________.
6. A room full of cards may be ________________. A small pile of cards is not.
7. With poor instructions, something with a few pieces may be ________________.
8. Even a small hill is ________________if it is too steep.
9. Because it lacks a consistent beat, a lot of jazz music is ________________.
10. If something is broken but cannot be fixed, it is ________________.

Check off these words as you use them.

unpaintable	unclimbable	undanceable	uncomfortable	unreadable
uncountable	unlaughable	unteachable	unbuildable	unrepairable

PREFIX/SUFFIX SQUARE

for un- meaning "not, or opposite of"
plus -ing, meaning "going on, happening now"

Start in the middle square with the prefix **un** and the suffix **ing** and combine both of these parts with the words in the other squares to build new words. Write each new word and the definition you can think of for it in the spaces provided at the bottom of the page.

seal	load	fasten
dress	**un-** + **-ing**	cover
fold	block	box

AFFIX ADDER

The prefix **un**- means "not, or opposite of."

The suffix –**ing** means "going on, happening now."

1. Write **un** in the blank space in front of each word and **ing** in the blank space after each word listed below and make a new word.
2. Tell what you think the new word means.
3. Write a sentence using the new word.

We've done one for you:

WIND means to twist around

...so UNWINDING means causing not to be twisted around.

Sentence: My brother was unwinding his tangled kite string.

---

1. DRESS means to put on

...so ____DRESS____ means ____________________________________

Used in a sentence:

---

2. FASTEN means to join together

...so ____FASTEN____ means ____________________________________

Used in a sentence:

---

3. FOLD means to double over

...so ____FOLD____ means ____________________________________

Used in a sentence:

---

4. COVER means to place something on top of

...so ____COVER____ means ____________________________________

Used in a sentence:

---

5. LOAD means to fill
...so ___LOAD___ means ____

6. PACK means to put into suitcases or boxes
...so ___PACK___ means ____

7. SEAL means to close tightly
...so ___SEAL___ means ____

8. TWIST means to turn or wind up
...so ___TWIST___ means ____

9. GROUP means to put together
...so ___GROUP___ means ____

10. HOOK means to fasten
...so ___HOOK___ means ____

MAGIC SQUARE

for **un**- meaning "not, or opposite of"

plus -**ing** meaning "going on, happening now"

Select the best definition for each of the words in the **un** plus **ing** family. Put the number of the definition in the proper space in the Magic Square box. If the numbers going up and down and the numbers going across all add up to the same thing, you have found the magic number!

WORDS

A. unsorting
B. uncluttering
C. unpacking
D. unsticking
E. undoing
F. unlatching
G. undressing
H. unbending
I. unearthing

DEFINITIONS

1. digging up out of the ground
2. taking away an action
3. not putting into specific piles
4. not gluing on
5. taking clothes out of a suitcase
6. making straight
7. making not messy or confused
8. taking clothes off
9. not locking

Magic Square Box

A.	B.	C.
D.	E.	F.
G.	H.	I.

Magic Number ______

Name ____________________________

WORD SEARCH

Words with prefix un- meaning "not, or opposite of"
and suffix -ing, meaning "going on, happening now"

Find and circle all the words in the grid. Words can go across or up and down, straight or diagonally, forwards or backwards.

```
G Z U G G U N C L E N C H I N G D G D J
N U J N D N K G J G M Q X H F L M H G C
I M N R H W I D Q L N V Q U M K R N G Y
N L T C L A N T P K C I N Q U N I T J T
E M G Z L R M Q C M B G K N Y N F L G J
T U N D P U L P W U U K W S E F G V N L
S N I G K T T L E A R I W D A N M N I G
A L T M J C G T R R S T R T I M G J K N
F O L C X T R D E H I U S D M N N J C I
N A O K M C I F I R B N A B I R N U A N
U D B H D N R N F N I E G L O M H H P E
U I N V G K G T U G R N I K R N R M N F
N N U J M N B N J H K E G Y K R U C U F
C G L N V B Q T T B V M J D R X K C K I
U C P L V F N N G N I H C T A L N U R T
R K F F L P U L U L J X F K C X P M G S
L K X M U N F U R L I N G W D R W R L N
I K M R T B T L U N S T A I N I N G T U
N M W N V L G N I N I A H C N U L R K L
G K T L X N Q N H G N I D E E H N U K R
```

unbolting	unfurling	unobstructing
unburdening	unguarding	unpacking
unchaining	unhampering	unstaining
unclenching	unheeding	unstiffening
uncluttering	unlatching	unthreading
uncurling	unloading	unveiling
unfastening	unmasking	unwishing

Not Right Now!

Fill in the blanks using the words below that all mean "not doing or opposite of something right now."
Why do they mean not doing or opposite of something right now?

____

1. "You can't come in. I'm ______________ so I can change my clothes."
2. James and Bart are ______________ the truck right now.
3. Jamilla is ______________ her kite string so she can fly her kite again.
4. Maria is ______________ her hair because she likes it straight.
5. Mom and Dad are ______________ from their trip.
6. Jules and Jamal are ______________ all the tape they used to put up pictures.
7. Flozelle is ______________ the note Lupe gave him after class.
8. Macey and Shawna are ______________ the big mess they made.
9. Detective Jones is ______________ clues about the stolen car.
10. Willy is ______________ the road so our car can get through.

Check off these words as you use them.

unpacking	unloading	unfolding	undoing	uncurling
untwisting	unsticking	uncovering	undressing	unblocking

PREFIX/SUFFIX SQUARE

for **re**- meaning "again, back, or against"

plus -**ed**, meaning "did before now, in the past"

Start in the middle square with the prefix **re** and the suffix **ed** and combine both of these parts with the words in the other squares to build new words. Write each new word and the definition you can think of for it in the spaces provided at the bottom of the page.

heat	gain	seal
wash	**re-** + **-ed**	fill
fold	print	count

AFFIX ADDER

The prefix re- means "again, back, or against."
The suffix –ed means "did before now, in the past."

1. Write **re** in the blank space in front of each word and **ed** in the blank space after each word listed below and make a new word.
2. Tell what you think the new word means.
3. Write a sentence using the new word.

We've done one for you:

PAINT means to apply a coating to
...so <u>RE</u>PAINT<u>ED</u> means <u>applied a coating to again.</u>
<u>Sentence</u>: We repainted our house last year.

____

1. MIX means to blend or to stir in
...so ____ MIX ____ means ______________________________
<u>Used in a sentence</u>:

____

2. ACT means to do
...so ____ ACT____ means ______________________________
<u>Used in a sentence</u>:

____

3. GATHER means to cause to come together
...so ____ GATHER____ means ______________________________
<u>Used in a sentence</u>:

____

4. DESIGN means to create

...so ____ DESIGN____ means ____

Used in a sentence:

5. GROUP means to gather together

...so ____ GROUP____ means ____

Used in a sentence:

6. HEAT means to warm

...so ____ HEAT____ means ____

Used in a sentence:

7. ORDER means to arrange

...so ____ ORDER____ means ____

Used in a sentence:

8. PLANT means to put something in the ground

...so ____ PLANT____ means ____

Used in a sentence:

9. SEAL means to close tightly

...so ____ SEAL____ means ____

Used in a sentence:

10. VIEW means to see

...so ____ VIEW____ means ____

MAGIC SQUARE

for **re**- meaning "again, back, or against"

plus -**ed**, meaning "did before now, in the past"

Select the best definition for each of the words in the **re** and **ed** families. Put the number of the definition in the proper space in the Magic Square box. If the numbers going up and down and the numbers going across all add up to the same thing, you have found the magic number!

WORDS

A. reinvented
B. refilled
C. remixed
D. rejoined
E. reformed
F. reopened
G. replanted
H. retrained
I. recleaned

DEFINITIONS

1. took off the dirt again
2. became a member of again
3. made complete or full again
4. changed the shape of again
5. stirred together again
6. put into the soil to grow again
7. found or discovered again
8. taught again
9. took off the cover again

Magic Square Box

A.	B.	C.
D.	E.	F.
G.	H.	I.

Magic Number ______

Name ______________________

WORD SEARCH

Words with prefix re- meaning "again, back, or against"
and suffix -ed, "meaning happened before now, in the past"

Find and circle all the words in the grid. Words can go across or up and down, straight or diagonally, forwards or backwards.

G	R	E	E	N	T	E	R	E	D	L	C	F	B	R	B	Y
R	N	V	W	R	D	E	R	E	D	I	S	N	O	C	E	R
L	Q	B	V	F	E	N	T	X	P	D	M	K	G	D	W	E
D	W	R	J	R	K	C	G	H	E	M	P	V	E	M	J	F
E	D	K	L	T	E	F	L	N	Z	T	L	T	M	H	G	O
T	Y	E	Q	K	D	F	E	A	G	X	C	T	D	Y	R	L
N	R	D	T	P	D	P	A	R	I	E	D	E	T	R	E	D
A	M	E	J	N	O	E	E	S	R	M	R	J	E	D	C	E
L	Q	N	W	E	E	G	K	I	T	A	E	C	L	E	O	D
P	M	G	R	O	A	V	D	O	E	E	O	D	P	W	L	G
E	N	I	N	I	R	E	N	P	O	N	N	M	W	E	L	D
R	P	S	N	T	R	D	P	I	N	C	X	E	N	N	E	E
L	K	E	T	R	B	A	E	E	E	P	E	N	D	E	C	T
J	D	D	K	Q	E	B	C	D	Q	R	K	R	C	R	T	C
K	T	E	T	R	T	T	D	E	T	A	E	H	E	R	E	A
L	B	R	Y	R	E	A	T	T	E	M	P	T	E	D	D	E
R	X	R	Y	D	R	E	P	R	I	N	T	E	D	F	B	R

reacted	recooked	reheated
reappeared	redesigned	reinvented
reattempted	redirected	renewed
reclaimed	reentered	reopened
recollected	refastened	replanted
reconnected	refolded	reprinted
reconsidered	regained	reworded

You did it again!

Fill in the blanks using the words below that all mean "did something again."

Why do they mean did something again? ____

1. The waitress ________________ my glass when it was empty.
2. The cashier ________________ the money I had already counted.
3. I enjoyed the new CD so much that I ________________ it over and over.
4. Kate ________________ her bedroom because she didn't like the old color.
5. I got home late from practice, so I ________________ my dinner in the microwave.
6. Marika's computer crashed, so she ________________ it.
7. The stain didn't come out the first time, so Mario ________________ his shirt.
8. My father ________________ the box so he could return it.
9. Suzanne didn't like where the peach tree was, so she ________________ it.
10. Antwan ________________ John's sentence so we could understand it.

Check off these words as you use them.

replayed	replanted	recounted	resealed	reheated
repainted	rewashed	reworded	restarted	refilled

PREFIX SQUARE

for **super**- meaning "over and above; beyond"

Start in the middle square with the prefix **super** and combine this part with the words in the other squares to build new words. Write each word and a definition you can think of for it in the spaces provided at the bottom of the page.

star	hero	power
charged	**super-**	market
highway	natural	fine

AFFIX ADDER

The prefix super- means "over and above; beyond."

1. Write **super** in the blank space in front of each word listed below and make a new word.
2. Tell what you think the new word means.
3. Write a sentence using the new word.

We've done one for you:

HUMAN means a man, woman, or child
...so SUPERHUMAN means having qualities above or beyond a regular man, woman, or child.

Sentence: World-class athletes such as those at the Olympics are capable of superhuman performances.

---

1. ABUNDANT means plentiful
...so ________ABUNDANT means ______________________________
Used in a sentence:

____

2. STAR means an outstandingly talented performer
...so ______STAR means ______________________________
Used in a sentence:

____

3. HIGHWAY means a major paved road
...so ______HIGHWAY means ______________________________
Used in a sentence:

____

4. LINER means a passenger ship
...so ______LINER means ______________________________
Used in a sentence:

____

5. NATURAL means as expected in the real world
...so ______ NATURAL means ______________________________
Used in a sentence:

____

6. ACHIEVER means a person who meets a goal
...so ______ACHIEVER means ______________________________
Used in a sentence:

____

7. HERO means a person who does some great deed
...so ______HERO means ______________________________
Used in a sentence:

____

8. FINE means very small
...so ______FINE means ______________________________
Used in a sentence:

____

9. MARKET means a place where things can be bought
...so ______MARKET means ______________________________
Used in a sentence:

____

10. HEAT means to raise the temperature
...so ______HEAT means ______________________________
Used in a sentence:

____

MAGIC SQUARE

for **super**- meaning "over and above; beyond"

Select the best definition for each of the words in the **super** family. Put the number of the definition in the proper space in the Magic Square box. If the numbers going up and down and the numbers going across all add up to the same thing, you have found the magic number!

WORDS

A. supercool
B. superstar
C. superpower
D. supercharge
E. supervision
F. superhighway
G. superabundant
H. superhero
I. supermom

DEFINITIONS

1. a cartoon or movie character with superhuman powers
2. to greatly increase the power of
3. a nation with great strength and influence
4. a major road
5. a movie star or sports figure
6. available in a supply over and above the normal
7. to bring to a temperature beyond a normal low
8. a woman who keeps house, takes care of children, and holds down a job
9. the job of watching over the work of others

Magic Square Box

A.	B.	C.
D.	E.	F.
G.	H.	I.

Magic Number ______

Name ______________________

WORD SEARCH

Words with the prefix super- meaning "over and above; beyond"

Find and circle the words in the grid. Words can go across or up and down, straight or diagonally, forwards or backwards

N	B	C	P	J	S	U	P	E	R	V	I	S	I	O	N	P	R	T	S
M	R	Y	L	F	E	Z	S	S	K	C	R	G	H	Y	P	R	T	T	U
N	E	C	S	L	G	M	U	K	U	Q	W	K	T	N	N	A	Z	E	P
H	N	W	U	O	R	K	P	C	K	P	T	Z	J	R	E	H	J	N	E
Y	I	R	P	O	A	K	E	R	K	P	E	Q	F	H	N	K	T	I	R
P	L	Z	E	C	H	F	R	L	R	R	F	R	R	B	L	K	N	F	A
F	R	H	R	R	C	G	H	V	A	J	S	E	W	K	K	D	W	R	B
R	E	P	A	E	R	X	E	Q	B	R	P	U	S	E	T	C	T	E	U
F	P	N	T	P	E	Q	R	D	Z	U	U	U	P	F	A	E	M	P	N
D	U	W	H	U	P	R	O	Q	S	E	P	T	K	E	K	P	N	U	D
X	S	J	L	S	U	C	P	R	X	E	R	S	A	R	R	Y	O	S	A
S	U	P	E	R	S	T	A	R	R	O	U	O	A	N	F	H	X	N	N
B	G	B	T	W	P	V	K	A	S	P	F	M	T	R	R	L	I	R	T
X	V	R	E	K	B	Z	C	I	E	D	R	L	N	S	N	E	R	T	Q
D	K	B	L	P	T	H	V	R	Z	E	N	L	L	L	R	B	P	T	K
D	L	L	H	Z	I	R	H	K	P	X	Q	J	N	X	L	E	B	U	P
C	K	L	L	E	E	U	K	U	M	L	E	D	O	M	R	E	P	U	S
L	P	D	V	P	M	C	S	Y	A	W	H	G	I	H	R	E	P	U	S
R	M	E	U	A	Q	M	L	F	J	N	T	G	D	N	G	V	R	R	S
V	R	S	N	Z	K	V	Y	X	L	S	U	P	E	R	S	W	E	E	T

superabundant	superhero	supernatural
superachiever	superhighway	superstar
superathlete	superhit	superstore
supercharge	superhuman	supersweet
supercool	superliner	supervision
superfine	supermarket	supervisor
superheat	supermodel	superweapon

TO THE MAX!

Fill in the blanks using the words below that all mean "over, above, or beyond something."

Why do they mean over, above, or beyond something? ______________________

1. Elves, fairies, leprechauns, and other ______________creatures appear in legend.
2. Insects are ______________, so birds and frogs have plenty to eat.
3. Although he looked like a regular guy, Clark Kent had ______________X-ray vision.
4. A dancer, singer, and actor all in one, Sasha is truly a ______________.
5. The Bibb family took a cruise on a huge ______________across the Atlantic.
6. The silky, ______________sand at the beach was as soft as powder.
7. Thanks to the ____________system, a car can go coast-to-coast with no stop sign.
8. Edna found everything she needed for the banquet at the ______________.
9. Teddy is a good independent worker who hardly ever needs ______________.
10. What countries will be the military ______________of the next generation?

Check off these words as you use them.

superabundant	superfine	superhighway	superhuman	superliner
supermarket	supernatural	superpowers	superstar	supervision

PREFIX SQUARE

for **sub**- meaning "under, below, or beneath"

Start in the middle square with the prefix **sub** and combine this part with the words in the other squares to build new words. Write each word and a definition you can think of for it in the spaces provided at the bottom of the page.

title	group	way
freezing	**sub-**	soil
tract	teen	standard

AFFIX ADDER

The prefix sub- means "under, below, or beneath."

1. Write **sub** in the blank space in front of each word listed below and make a new word.
2. Tell what you think the new word means.
3. Write a sentence using the new word.

We've done one for you:

MARINE means ocean

...so SUBMARINE means below the surface of the ocean.

Sentence: A nuclear submarine can stay underwater for months at a time.

1. HUMAN means like a person

...so ____ HUMAN means ____________________

Used in a sentence:

2. NORMAL means what is expected

...so ____ NORMAL means ____________________

Used in a sentence:

3. SOIL means the top layer of the earth's surface

...so ____ SOIL means ____________________

Used in a sentence:

4. STANDARD means the accepted quality or model

...so ____ STANDARD means ____________________

Used in a sentence.

5. WAY means passage or route
...so ____ WAY means ______________________________________

Used in a sentence:

____

6. TEEN means a person of ages between twelve and twenty
...so ____ TEEN means ______________________________________

Used in a sentence:

____

7. COMPACT means occupying little space
...so ____ COMPACT means ______________________________________

Used in a sentence:

____

8. CONTINENT means one of the large geographic areas of the earth
...so ____ CONTINENT means ______________________________________

Used in a sentence:

____

9. DIVIDE means to separate into smaller pieces
...so ____ DIVIDE means ______________________________________

Used in a sentence:

____

10. FREEZING means temperature at which liquid water turns to ice
...so ____ FREEZING means ______________________________________

Used in a sentence:

____

MAGIC SQUARE

for **sub**- meaning "under, below, or beneath"

Select the best definition for each of the words in the **sub** family. Put the number of the definition in the proper space in the Magic Square box. If the numbers going up and down and the numbers going across all add up to the same thing, you have found the magic number!

WORDS

A. subsoil
B. submarine
C. subdivided
D. subnormal
E. subfloor
F. subway
G. subzero
H. subplot
I. subtitle

DEFINITIONS

1. a story line happening beneath another story
2. with qualities that fall short of the usual or regular
3. broken down more into smaller sections
4. a passageway or train that runs underground
5. beneath the surface of the water; a ship that travels under water
6. lower than nothing; very cold
7. dirt beneath the top layer of ground
8. the name of a piece of writing that goes beneath the main name
9. a layer of support beneath another flat surface

Magic Square Box

A.	B.	C.
D.	E.	F.
G.	H.	I.

Magic Number ______

Name ___________________________

WORD SEARCH

Words with the prefix sub- meaning "under or below or beneath"

Find and circle all the words in the grid. Words can go across or up and down, straight or diagonally, forwards or backwards.

K	D	R	A	D	N	A	T	S	B	U	S	C	F	B	N	S
K	D	S	S	U	B	C	O	N	T	R	A	C	T	N	T	U
T	S	T	U	P	E	L	C	K	N	S	G	H	Y	N	R	B
C	T	U	F	B	T	S	Y	J	U	W	M	F	E	P	S	S
A	E	L	B	J	S	A	A	B	W	T	G	N	M	U	K	C
P	E	T	Z	D	W	C	T	E	E	W	I	F	B	G	S	R
M	N	K	U	B	I	I	R	G	L	T	G	F	M	S	U	I
O	I	P	U	T	T	V	R	I	N	B	R	R	U	L	B	P
C	R	S	L	L	I	E	I	O	B	E	U	B	N	A	D	T
B	A	L	E	K	M	T	C	S	E	E	S	S	V	T	U	I
U	M	T	C	B	N	B	S	Z	I	O	H	N	V	O	C	O
S	B	R	U	N	U	L	I	B	I	O	C	E	X	T	T	N
D	U	S	K	S	W	N	T	L	U	T	N	E	X	B	I	F
W	S	M	N	H	G	N	M	M	K	S	B	T	L	U	O	T
K	R	J	P	N	C	W	N	A	M	U	H	B	U	S	N	T
N	T	S	U	B	N	O	R	M	A	L	B	U	R	L	M	N
T	C	A	R	T	B	U	S	D	T	X	K	S	P	R	Z	B

subcompact	sublease	substandard
subcontinent	submarine	substitute
subcontract	submerge	subteen
subdivision	subnormal	subtitle
subduction	subscribe	subtotal
subfreezing	subscription	subtract
subhuman	subsoil	subway

LET ME OUT!

Fill in the blanks using the words below that all mean "under something".

Why do they mean under something? ______________________________

1. A _________________ is a ship that travels underwater.
2. A _________________ climate is very hot and sticky.
3. Jamar added up the _______________ of our food before tax and tip.
4. Mary had to _________________ her dress in water to clean it.
5. A really small car is called a ________________.
6. Coach had to ________________ the team into smaller groups for drills.
7. Monkeys are considered less than human, or _________________.
8. I belong to a ________________ of my class that is studying butterflies.
9. A particle smaller than an atom is called _________________.
10. A really cold climate is called _______________, the opposite of subtropical.

Check off these words as you use them.

subtotal	subhuman	submarine	submerge	subdivide
subarctic	subcompact	subatomic	subtropical	subgroup

SUFFIX SQUARE

for -**hood** meaning "a group that shares some characteristic"

Start in the middle square with the suffix **hood** and combine this part with the words in the other squares to build new words. Write each word and a definition you can think of for it in the spaces provided at the bottom of the page.

state	adult	child
brother	**-hood**	sister
nation	saint	false

AFFIX ADDER

The suffix -hood means "a group that shares some characteristic."

1. Write **hood** in the blank space after each word listed below and make a new word.
2. Tell what you think the new word means.
3. Write a sentence using the new word.

We've done one for you:

STATE means a political unit

...so STATEHOOD means a group that shares the political unit.

Sentence: Hawaii was granted statehood in 1959.

1. ADULT means a person of mature and legal age

...so ADULT______ means ____________________________________

Used in a sentence:

2. BABY means a person of infant age

...so BABY______ means ____________________________________

Used in a sentence:

3. FALSE means untrue

...so FALSE______ means ____________________________________

Used in a sentence:

4. GRANDPARENT means parent of the parent of a child

...so GRANDPARENT ______ means ____________________________________

Used in a sentence:

5. SISTER refers to a female sibling

...so SISTER_____ means ______________________________

Used in a sentence:

6. NEIGHBOR means a person who lives nearby

...so NEIGHBOR_____ means ______________________________

Used in a sentence:

7. KNIGHT refers to a man in service to a king

...so KNIGHT_____ means ______________________________

Used in a sentence:

8. GOD refers to a heavenly being that is worshiped by people

...so GOD _____ means ______________________________

Used in a sentence:

9. WOMAN refers to an adult female

...so WOMAN_____ means ______________________________

Used in a sentence:

10. BACHELOR refers to an unmarried adult male

...so BACHELOR _____ means______________________________

Used in a sentence:

MAGIC SQUARE

for -**hood** meaning "a group that shares some characteristic"

Select the best definition for each of the words in the suffix **hood** family. Put the number of the definition in the proper space in the Magic Square box. If the numbers going up and down and the numbers going across all add up to the same thing, you have found the magic number!

WORDS

A. adulthood
B. boyhood
C. girlhood
D. falsehood
E. maidhood
F. motherhood
G. orphanhood
H. widowhood
I. selfhood

DEFINITIONS

1. condition of owing a lot of money
2. state of being a young female
3. state of a woman whose husband has died
4. condition of not being true
5. condition of being a young person whose parents have died
6. state of being a female parent
7. state of being a young male
8. state of working as a female servant
9. state of being grown up
10. the state of having individual identity

Magic Square Box

A.	B.	C.
D.	E.	F.
G.	H.	I.

Magic Number ______

Name ____________________

WORD SEARCH

Words with the suffix -hood, meaning "a group that shares some characteristic"

Find and circle all the words in the grid. Words can go across or up and down, straight or diagonally, forwards or backwards

H	V	X	G	P	Y	K	R	D	T	Y	J	J	P	M	Y	Z	X
L	Q	Q	K	T	R	D	O	M	D	L	M	Y	M	G	G	C	R
T	N	R	T	B	O	O	T	D	O	O	H	R	E	H	T	A	F
T	Q	H	K	O	H	Z	R	B	O	Y	H	O	O	D	M	M	K
R	V	X	H	Y	M	A	I	D	E	N	H	O	O	D	N	D	H
N	G	N	B	D	W	B	A	C	H	E	L	O	R	H	O	O	D
K	A	A	T	N	O	K	H	M	M	X	D	X	N	O	W	S	R
M	B	N	D	E	D	O	B	P	C	G	L	O	H	M	A	T	D
C	D	A	O	I	O	Y	H	R	A	H	I	R	O	I	M	F	X
H	O	T	O	G	O	N	N	R	O	R	E	R	N	H	A	Y	L
I	O	I	H	H	H	Y	N	G	E	T	E	T	L	L	D	Y	R
L	H	O	T	B	T	N	T	R	S	H	H	N	S	H	K	O	Y
D	N	N	H	O	L	V	T	I	W	O	T	E	T	Y	O	K	G
H	A	H	G	R	U	K	S	F	O	L	H	O	R	H	M	O	W
O	M	O	I	H	D	G	R	D	T	O	L	M	M	H	O	N	D
O	O	O	N	O	A	G	L	C	O	C	N	B	K	X	O	O	K
D	W	D	K	O	P	J	V	D	N	Z	F	R	L	T	C	O	D
L	R	M	T	D	Y	G	D	O	O	H	E	T	A	T	S	M	D

adulthood	fatherhood	nationhood
babyhood	girlhood	neighborhood
bachelorhood	godhood	parenthood
boyhood	knighthood	sainthood
brotherhood	maidenhood	sisterhood
childhood	manhood	statehood
falsehood	motherhood	womanhood

You see, it's like this….

Fill in the blanks using the words at the bottom of the page that all mean "a group that shares some characteristic."
Why do they mean group that shares some characteristic? ____________________

1. Bibs, highchairs, and peek-a-boo are features of our ________________.
2. Alaska and Hawaii both gained ________________ in 1959.
3. In my _____________ years ages six to ten, my family always went on beach trips.
4. The _____________ of the belief that the earth was flat was clear to early sailors.
5. All of the garage doors in my ________________ are painted brown.
6. The rock star was given ________________ by the Queen.
7. The women shared their experiences about their children and other aspects of ________________.
8. Our dog Fido spent his ________________ playing stick-catch in the back yard.
9. Best friends Tom and Charlie are an example of good-natured ________________.
10. The girls joined together in a ____________ and pledged to work for good causes.

Check off these words as you use them.

babyhood	brotherhood	childhood	falsehood	knighthood
motherhood	neighborhood	puppyhood	sisterhood	statehood

SUFFIX SQUARE

for **-ness** meaning "condition or quality"

Start in the middle square with the suffix **ness** and combine this part with the words in the other squares to build new words. Write each word and a definition you can think of for it in the spaces provided at the bottom of the page.

fair	neat	calm
good	**-ness**	kind
weak	mean	dark

AFFIX ADDER

The suffix -ness means "condition or quality."

1. Write **ness** in the blank space after each word listed below and make a new word.
2. Tell what you think the new word means.
3. Write a sentence using the new word.

We've done one for you:

KIND means friendly and tending to care for others
...so KIND<u>NESS</u> means <u>the quality of friendliness and care for others.</u>
<u>Sentence</u>: Human kindness is an important quality in a person.

---

1. GENTLE means considerate and tender
...so GENTLE ______ means ______________________________
<u>Used in a sentence</u>:

---

2. DULL means not sharp
...so DULL ______ means ______________________________
<u>Used in a sentence</u>:

---

3. COLD means having a low temperature
...so COLD ______ means ______________________________
<u>Used in a sentence</u>:

---

4. WIDE means broad
...so WIDE ______ means ______________________________
<u>Used in a sentence</u>:

---

5. BALD means without hair

...so BALD______ means ____

<u>Used in a sentence</u>:

6. LATE means delayed

...so LATE ______ means ____

<u>Used in a sentence</u>:

7. OPEN means providing clear entrance

...so OPEN______ means ____

<u>Used in a sentence</u>:

8. GOOD means positive and desirable

...so GOOD ______ means ____

<u>Used in a sentence</u>:

9. NUMB means without feeling

...so NUMB ______ means ____

<u>Used in a sentence</u>:

10. HELPFUL means ready and able to lend aid

...so HELPFUL______ means ____

<u>Used in a sentence</u>:

MAGIC SQUARE

for -**ness** meaning "condition or quality"

Select the best definition for each of the words in the **-ness** family. Put the number of the definition in the proper space in the Magic Square box. If the numbers going up and down and the numbers going across all add up to the same thing, you have found the magic number!

WORDS

A. madness
B. calmness
C. darkness
D. fullness
E. blindness
F. wellness
G. fitness
H. weakness
I. dampness

DEFINITIONS

1. condition of being without strength
2. condition of not being empty
3. quality of being without light
4. quality of being in good health
5. condition of rest, peace, and quiet
6. quality of being in good shape or having physical ability
7. condition of being angry or out of one's mind
8. quality of being wet
9. condition of being without eyesight

Magic Square Box

A.	B.	C.
D.	E.	F.
G.	H.	I.

Magic Number ______

Name ________________________

WORD SEARCH

Words with the suffix -ness, meaning "condition or quality"

Find and circle all the words in the grid. Words can go across or up and down, straight or diagonally, forwards or backwards

V	L	Y	B	G	O	O	D	N	E	S	S	C	T	C	P	K
R	N	K	K	P	G	R	N	S	S	I	C	K	N	E	S	S
V	F	D	D	V	M	N	I	F	S	D	H	Y	X	S	N	F
M	J	C	J	N	W	S	X	P	I	E	T	R	E	K	S	N
V	B	B	L	J	J	S	S	N	E	R	N	N	T	S	P	M
M	Q	A	Z	Y	K	S	X	E	C	N	M	D	E	D	P	M
K	D	L	M	S	D	E	G	K	N	L	E	N	L	W	R	J
P	Y	D	P	S	A	N	L	N	A	D	D	S	E	I	N	N
N	S	N	N	E	M	R	A	C	J	L	N	A	S	S	M	S
E	S	E	S	N	P	I	D	R	O	W	K	O	S	K	S	H
A	E	S	S	E	N	A	N	B	M	N	Z	S	F	E	A	Q
T	N	S	E	G	E	F	E	Q	E	D	E	W	N	R	M	R
N	L	L	N	N	S	Q	S	S	J	N	N	E	D	W	R	R
E	L	X	N	A	S	C	S	P	E	K	C	N	G	M	L	J
S	I	F	A	R	R	N	R	D	R	I	E	F	W	R	F	Q
S	T	Y	E	T	J	T	I	R	N	S	L	B	N	K	C	N
R	S	C	M	S	G	W	Z	S	S	E	N	R	A	E	D	C

baldness	fondness	niceness
boldness	gladness	ripeness
calmness	goodness	sickness
dampness	hardness	stillness
dearness	meanness	strangeness
fairness	mildness	weakness
firmness	neatness	wideness

How is it?

Fill in the blanks using the words at the bottom of the page that all mean "condition or quality of something."
Why do they mean condition or quality of something? ______________________

1. From the ______________ of their hearts Ken and Sheila returned the wallet they found.

2. In winter days, ______________ falls by about 4 o'clock.

3. Joline says she has a ______________ for anything chocolate.

4. The qualities of ____________ and readability on written work are important.

5. The _________ of the summer evening was broken only by an occasional cricket.

6. The ______________ of her touch calmed the frightened dog.

7. Because of the ______________ in the day, the director called off play practice.

8. The ______________ of the neighbors made the job of moving in much easier.

9. The ______________ of the earth made transplanting the tree an easy job.

10. The ______________ of the new city caused us to get lost five times.

Check off these words as you use them.

calmness	dampness	darkness	gentleness	goodness
helpfulness	lateness	neatness	strangeness	weakness

PREFIX SQUARE

for **fore**- meaning "before; earlier; in front of"

Start in the middle square with the prefix **fore** and combine this part with the words in the other squares to build new words. Write each word and a definition you can think of for it in the spaces provided at the bottom of the page.

thought	word	fathers
ground	**fore-**	head
runner	see	tell

AFFIX ADDER

The prefix fore- means "before; earlier; in front of."

1. Write **fore** in the blank space in front of each word listed below and make a new word.
2. Tell what you think the new word means.
3. Write a sentence using the new word.

We've done one for you:

THOUGHT means the act or process of thinking

...so FORE THOUGHT means the act of thinking before.

Sentence: A grocery list is an example of forethought on paper.

1. GROUND means a defined area or space

...so ______GROUND means ______________________________

Used in a sentence:

____

2. HEAD means the top part of the body

...so ______HEAD means ______________________________

Used in a sentence:

____

3. CAST means to send forth or to guess

...so ______CAST means ______________________________

Used in a sentence:

____

4. SIGHT means vision

...so ______SIGHT means ______________________________

Used in a sentence:

____

5. TELL means to say or to speak something
...so ______TELL means ________________________________
Used in a sentence:

6. WARN means to caution
...so ______WARN means ________________________________
Used in a sentence:

7. ARMED means furnished with tools of defense
...so ______ARMED means ________________________________
Used in a sentence:

8. KNOWLEDGE means information
...so ______KNOWLEDGE means ________________________________
Used in a sentence:

9. TASTE is the sense that perceives flavor
...so ______TASTE means ________________________________
Used in a sentence:

10. BODE means to give promise of
...so ______BODE means ________________________________
Used in a sentence:

MAGIC SQUARE

for **fore**- meaning "before; earlier; in front of"

Select the best definition for each of the words in the **fore** family. Put the number of the definition in the proper space in the Magic Square box. If the numbers going up and down and the numbers going across all add up to the same thing, you have found the magic number!

WORDS

A. foredeck
B. forestall
C. foretell
D. foresight
E. forerunner
F. forepaw
G. forehead
H. foreword
I. forethought

DEFINITIONS

1. to sound an alarm or caution before something occurs
2. to delay or to put off
3. thinking that happens beforehand
4. the ability to see ahead
5. the part of the face that is above the eyebrows
6. something or someone coming before another thing or event
7. to say before an event occurs
8. the foot of an animal's front leg
9. the flat surface at the front of a boat or ship
10. an introduction at the front of a book or story

Magic Square Box

A.	B.	C.
D.	E.	F.
G.	H.	I.

Magic Number ______

Name ______________________

WORD SEARCH

Words with the prefix fore- meaning "before; earlier; in front of"

Find and circle the words in the grid. Words can go across or up and down, straight of diagonally, forwards or backwards.

```
M W A P E R O F N Y F O R E G R O U N D
B B G N V M J X M P P Z P L E F N F L Y
Q R N M V M M K Z M H T J E O W T O P B
T K F V H F B V B M L F S R L L T R K R
L S B O F W T Z H Q Q E E P Z E K E X T
Q L A F R R Q P F L R W X P R J N F N K
D N A C F E J T F O A P T O Z P K A F W
C P N T E O W O F R G L F L F W D T O N
B K Z H S R R O N C K V V G O M P H R M
T C K G N E O E R K B V R N R K Q E E Y
H F K K H Y R F T D K C M I E F Q R T T
G Q L E H D L O E A K B Z D K D P S E R
U K A M L F M M F B S M T O N N K L L H
O D M V R R R R N G X T M B O A H X L V
H Y V J M A M R L V G R E E W H N D H L
T K G G E F O R E D E C K R L E B R X N
E C P R Q K Q P N R C Z K O E R Z T N D
R N O W O D A H S E R O F F D O D M N R
O F M G F O R E S I G H T Z G F P T T Y
F W R R E N N U R E R O F D E B T B Y R
```

forearmed	forehead	forestall
foreboding	foreknowledge	foretaste
forecast	forepaw	foretell
foredeck	forerunner	forethought
forefathers	foresee	foretold
foreground	foreshadow	forewarn
forehand	foresight	foreword

Before!

Fill in the blanks using the words below that all mean "before, earlier, or in front of something."

Why do they mean before, earlier, or in front of something? ______________________

1. In the ________________ of the picture you'll see Aunt Hannah's chickens.
2. Someone must have given Skip the ________________ about his surprise party.
3. The clues that an author gives on the first page ________________ later events.
4. The prophet in the epic _______________to the hero his upcoming adventures.
5. Because the hero had been ________________, he was able to protect himself.
6. Trish said her ________________ came to this country from three continents.
7. Ruth has a powerful ________________ stroke in tennis.
8. My cat Inky had a thorn in its right ________________.
9. The first stop was just a _____________ of the wonderful vacation we would have.
10. In the _____________, the author thanked those who had helped with the writing.

Check off these words as you use them.

forefathers	foreground	forehand	foreknowledge	forepaw
foreshadow	foretaste	foretells	forewarned	foreword

SUFFIX SQUARE

for -**ed** meaning "did before now, in the past" with doubling

Start in the middle square with the suffix **ed** and combine this part with the words in the other squares to build new words. Remember to double the final consonant of the words to which you attach the suffix **ed**. Write each word and a definition you can think of for it in the spaces provided at the bottom of the page.

stop	chat	skid
hop	**-ed**	hug
clip	grin	rub

AFFIX ADDER

The suffix -ed means "did before now, in the past."

When –ed is attached to a one-syllable word ending in a consonant with a single vowel in front of it, the consonant is doubled.

1. Write **ed** in the blank space after each word listed below and make a new word. Remember to double the last letter.
2. Tell what you think the new word means.
3. Write a sentence using the new word.

We've done one for you:

SIP means to take small drinks

...so SIP<u>PED</u> means <u>took small drinks.</u>

<u>Sentence</u>: Juan sipped slowly on his lemonade.

____

1. GRAB means to take suddenly

...so GRAB______ means ______________________________

<u>Used in a sentence</u>:

____

2. SLAM means to shut noisily or push violently

...so SLAM______ means ______________________________

<u>Used in a sentence</u>:

____

3. NOD means to agree with a shake of the head

...so NOD______ means ______________________________

<u>Used in a sentence</u>:

____

4. STIR means to mix or move around

...so STIR______ means ______________________________

<u>Used in a sentence</u>:

5. WRAP means to cover

...so WRAP______ means ______________________________

<u>Used in a sentence</u>:

6. CAP means to put a lid on

...so CAP______ means______________________________

<u>Used in a sentence</u>:

7. SPOT means to see suddenly

...so SPOT______ means ______________________________

<u>Used in a sentence</u>:

8. DROP means to let fall

...so DROP______ means ______________________________

<u>Used in a sentence</u>:

9. TRIM means to decorate or cut back

...so TRIM______ means ______________________________

<u>Used in a sentence</u>:

10. PAT means to touch gently

...so PAT______ means ______________________________

<u>Used in a sentence</u>:

MAGIC SQUARE

for -**ed** meaning "did before now, in the past" with doubling

Select the best definition for each of the words in the **ed** with doubled consonant words family. Put the number of the definition in the proper space in the Magic Square box. If the numbers going up and down and the numbers going across all add up to the same thing, you have found the magic number!

WORDS

A. plugged
B. mopped
C. fanned
D. jammed
E. stirred
F. nodded
G. hopped
H. chatted
I. wagged

DEFINITIONS

1. hit up against suddenly
2. put a date on
3. calmed down
4. talked casually
5. cleaned up with a cloth on a stick
6. moved side to side
7. cooled by causing air to move
8. agreed silently
9. stopped up a hole or leak
10. took suddenly
11. jumped up and down
12. mixed or caused to move

Magic Square Box

A.	B.	C.
D.	E.	F.
G.	H.	I.

Magic Number _____

Name ___________________________

WORD SEARCH

Words with suffix -ed, meaning "did before now, in the past" with doubling

Find and circle the words in the grid. Words can go across or up and down, straight of diagonally, forwards or backwards.

L	X	Q	T	W	R	Q	N	D	E	B	B	A	R	G
X	P	C	K	I	P	D	E	T	T	O	P	S	D	F
D	G	A	M	R	F	W	D	Z	C	K	P	E	L	Z
D	I	M	T	M	M	M	E	P	W	W	P	T	K	D
W	E	M	F	T	Y	Q	G	R	Q	P	D	W	E	D
D	D	G	M	L	E	K	G	K	A	R	L	G	E	D
S	E	E	G	E	K	D	E	C	O	V	G	R	E	Z
T	P	D	N	A	D	T	B	P	B	U	R	D	P	K
O	P	I	N	N	W	W	P	T	H	I	D	F	L	D
P	A	P	V	T	I	E	M	W	T	I	H	B	U	E
P	R	P	X	M	D	R	H	S	K	T	K	M	G	P
E	W	E	T	R	V	H	G	S	V	Y	Z	T	G	P
D	M	D	K	P	X	C	H	A	T	T	E	D	E	O
D	E	P	P	I	S	L	N	O	D	D	E	D	D	H
K	Q	R	T	L	N	K	Z	Y	M	B	R	T	Z	T

begged	grinned	sipped
capped	hopped	skidded
chatted	hugged	spotted
dimmed	nodded	stirred
dipped	patted	stopped
dropped	plugged	wagged
grabbed	rimmed	wrapped

REPEAT!

Fill in the blanks using the words below that all mean "did something in the past."

Why do they mean did something in the past? ______________________________

1. Well-wishers gently _______________ Jeff on the back for his good deed.
2. We knew Mr. Perry was mad because he _______________ the door.
3. Suzie _______________ three bald eagles during her camping trip.
4. The gardener _______________ the hedges and weeded the flowerbed.
5. The vacationers _______________ off their trip with one last look back at the sea.
6. The caller at the spelling bee _______________ that I had gotten the word correct.
7. The class _______________ a big trip to the amusement park.
8. No one dared laugh when Miss Grim _______________ on the ice and fell down.
9. The people making apple butter _______________ the mixture continuously for an hour.
10. The temperature _______________ twenty degrees during the afternoon.

Check off these words as you use them.

capped	dropped	nodded	patted	planned
slammed	slipped	spotted	stirred	trimmed

SUFFIX SQUARE

for -ing, a describing word meaning "ongoing, or in progress now"

Start in the middle square with the suffix **ing** (adjective) and combine this part with the words in the other squares to build new words. Write each word and a definition you can think of for it in the spaces provided at the bottom of the page.

spread	leap	hang
gleam	**-ing**	flow
bark	ripen	bang

AFFIX ADDER

This suffix -ing creates a describing word meaning "ongoing, or in progress now."

1. Write **ing** in the blank space after each word listed below and make a new word.
2. Tell what you think the new word means.
3. Write a sentence using the new word.

We've done one for you:

CHEER means to encourage and applaud

...so CHEERING means encouraging or applauding now.

Sentence: The cheering fans are encouraging the team to victory.

1. COMFORT means to soothe

...so COMFORT___ means ______________________________

Used in a sentence:

2. CLIMB means to go up

...so CLIMB___ means ______________________________

Used in a sentence:

3. GLOW means to shine

...so GLOW ___ means ______________________________

Used in a sentence:

4. SINK means to go beneath the surface

...so SINK ___ means ______________________________

Used in a sentence:

5. HEAL means to make well

...so HEAL___ means ______________________________

Used in a sentence:

____

6. RUSH means to move fast

...so RUSH___ means ______________________________

Used in a sentence:

____

7. TRAVEL means to go from one place to another

...so TRAVEL___ means ______________________________

Used in a sentence:

____

8. FLY means to travel through the air

...so FLY_____ means ______________________________

Used in a sentence:

____

9. FALL means to tumble down

...so FALL_____ means ______________________________

Used in a sentence:

____

10. VISIT means to come to see

...so VISIT_____ means ______________________________

Used in a sentence:

____

MAGIC SQUARE

for **-ing**, creating a describing word meaning "ongoing, or in progress now"

Select the best definition for each of the words in the suffix **ing** (adjective) family. Put the number of the definition in the proper space in the Magic Square box. If the numbers going up and down and the numbers going across all add up to the same thing, you have found the magic number!

WORDS

A. trusting
B. steaming
C. sleeping
D. running
E. roaring
F. remaining
G. masking
H. marching
I. gathering

DEFINITIONS

1. in progress of moving along in rhythm
2. in progress of moving fast on foot
3. in a restful state
4. being left over
5. so hot as to be putting off vapor
6. covering up
7. having faith in
8. coming together into a mass
9. making a loud lion-like noise

Magic Square Box

A.	B.	C.
D.	E.	F.
G.	H.	I.

Magic Number ______

Name ______________________

WORD SEARCH

Words with suffix -ing, creating a describing word meaning "ongoing, or in progress now."

Find and circle all the words in the grid. Words can go across or up and down, straight or diagonally, forwards or backwards.

G	N	I	M	A	E	T	S	G	N	I	N	N	U	R	N
N	N	W	W	F	C	O	N	N	E	C	T	I	N	G	J
I	V	I	R	L	F	M	R	W	G	B	F	R	F	R	H
K	L	L	R	R	V	O	A	N	B	L	K	J	A	I	G
N	X	T	G	E	A	G	I	S	O	Q	T	W	L	P	N
I	R	R	N	R	H	D	N	A	K	V	C	M	L	E	I
S	K	J	I	C	A	T	T	I	G	I	D	G	I	N	P
C	L	N	K	E	R	I	A	G	H	G	N	J	N	I	E
G	G	V	R	G	N	A	V	G	N	S	M	G	G	N	E
N	V	P	A	G	W	G	W	I	G	I	U	P	M	G	L
I	S	T	B	R	N	L	K	L	M	X	T	R	J	M	S
G	T	K	L	I	R	C	H	T	I	K	K	S	T	Y	N
N	B	M	P	N	I	M	K	C	M	N	M	B	U	J	Q
A	M	A	L	L	L	X	B	W	B	P	G	R	M	R	T
H	E	K	C	R	G	N	I	W	O	L	F	M	N	D	T
L	C	M	A	R	C	H	I	N	G	R	D	T	M	K	R

barking	gathering	running
clicking	hanging	rushing
connecting	leaping	sinking
crawling	marching	sleeping
falling	masking	spreading
floating	ripening	steaming
flowing	roaring	trusting

DO IT RIGHT NOW!

Fill in the blanks using the words below that are describing words meaning "ongoing, or in progress now."
Why do they mean "ongoing, or in progress now"?

____

1. A nice __________________ breeze felt good on the hot day.
2. The __________________ stars looked like sparklers in the night sky.
3. We can actually see some __________________ satellites.
4. There was a __________________ passage between the kitchen and the dining room.
5. The __________________ waves looked like root beer floats.
6. The __________________ birds sounded just like a cat.
7. The ivy __________________ to the ground looked just like a carpet.
8. Some __________________ insects were marching in single file.
9. Visitors are afraid of my __________________ dog.
10. I need a long, __________________ vacation.

Check off these words as you use them.

clinging	cooling	foaming	growling	orbiting
connecting	crawling	glittering	mocking	relaxing

SUFFIX SQUARE

for **-ing**, which forms nouns meaning "an act or action"

Start in the middle square with the suffix **ing** (noun) and combine this part with the words in the other squares to build new words. Write each word and a definition you can think of for it in the spaces provided at the bottom of the page.

walk	talk	clean
end	**-ing**	draw
open	sight	scream

AFFIX ADDER

This suffix -ing creates a noun meaning "an act or action."

1. Write **ing** in the blank space after each word listed below and make a new word.
2. Tell what you think the new word means.
3. Write a sentence using the new word.

We've done one for you:

COOK means to prepare and heat for eating
...so COOK<u>ING</u> means <u>preparing for eating by heating.</u>
<u>Sentence</u>: Cooking is necessary for most foods before they can be eaten.

1. CAMP means to live temporarily outdoors
...so CAMP___ means ______________________________
<u>Used in a sentence</u>:

2. FISH means to try to catch fish
...so FISH___ means ______________________________
<u>Used in a sentence</u>:

3. FLOSS means to clean between your teeth
...so FLOSS___ means ______________________________
<u>Used in a sentence</u>:

4. GARDEN means to raise plants for food or flowers
...so GARDEN___ means ______________________________
<u>Used in a sentence</u>:

5. HUNT means to look for
...so HUNT___ means ________________________________
Used in a sentence:

6. SUBTRACT means to take away
...so SUBTRACT___ means ____________________________
Used in a sentence:

7. WORRY means to fret about
...so WORRY___ means _______________________________
Used in a sentence:

8. SAIL means to be pushed by the wind
...so SAIL _____ means _____________________________
Used in a sentence:

9. BANK means to save for the future
...so BANK_____ means ______________________________
Used in a sentence:

10. GREET means to welcome
...so GREET_____ means _____________________________
Used in a sentence:

MAGIC SQUARE

for -**ing** , which forms nouns meaning "an act or action"

Select the best definition for each of the words in the suffix **ing** (noun) family. Put the number of the definition in the proper space in the Magic Square box. If the numbers going up and down and the numbers going across all add up to the same thing, you have found the magic number!

WORDS

A. cooking
B. offering
C. printing
D. reading
E. singing
F. speeding
G. traveling
H. clowning
I. warning

DEFINITIONS

1. the act of taking things away
2. the act or skill of heating food for eating
3. a way to tell people that danger is near
4. the act of skill of making music out of words
5. the act of being silly
6. the act of enjoying books or other print
7. a style of writing in block letters
8. the act of going too fast
9. anything given
10. the act of visiting different places

Magic Square Box

A.	B.	C.
D.	E.	F.
G.	H.	I.

Magic Number ______

Name ____________________________

WORD SEARCH

Words with suffix -ing, creating a noun meaning "an act or action."

Find and circle all the words in the grid. Words can go across or up and down, straight or diagonally, forwards or backwards.

O	B	G	N	I	T	A	E	B	L	K	W	R	R	C	K
F	T	O	U	C	H	I	N	G	Q	A	Q	H	X	R	L
F	L	X	H	M	E	A	N	I	N	G	N	L	L	P	D
E	G	N	I	T	N	I	R	P	L	R	K	D	A	K	N
R	C	T	B	R	M	K	S	M	Z	B	D	R	I	L	K
I	V	J	R	A	Y	G	N	I	L	E	E	N	K	N	L
N	R	N	E	C	Z	K	W	G	N	N	J	P	L	D	G
G	G	R	B	V	X	O	T	N	T	G	C	F	M	N	F
Z	C	N	K	N	R	A	K	I	Z	T	I	G	I	G	S
S	Y	K	I	R	L	Q	N	N	R	P	R	N	J	N	P
H	J	Y	Y	K	B	G	K	A	D	X	W	I	G	I	E
T	L	I	I	D	N	R	M	E	K	O	P	D	V	H	E
X	N	N	F	M	N	A	K	L	L	J	T	A	Q	S	D
G	G	Y	L	Y	T	B	R	C	Y	T	T	E	Z	U	I
Y	B	W	D	G	N	I	K	L	A	W	Z	R	Y	R	N
S	H	O	W	I	N	G	D	R	A	W	I	N	G	R	G

beating	offering	showing
cleaning	parenting	singing
clowning	printing	speeding
drawing	ranking	talking
kneeling	reading	touching
landing	rushing	walking
meaning	screaming	worrying

I'm doing it, I'm doing it!

Fill in the blanks using the words below that all mean "an act or action."
Why do they mean an act or action? ________________________________

1. Shequita loves ________________ the tennis team.
2. The ships made a ________________ before the storm arose.
3. We actually keep warmer by the act of ________________.
4. Mabel had ________________ laid down on her floors.
5. We could hear the ________________ of the wolves in the night.
6. There is an old ________________, "You are what you eat."
7. The little boy's ________________ made me feel sad, too.
8. Some people get whatever they want by ________________ and being nasty.
9. No ________________ allowed in Hide and Go Seek!
10. Bees protect their nests by ________________.

Check off these words as you use them.

carpeting	complaining	landing	saying	stinging
coaching	howling	peeping	shivering	weeping

SUFFIX SQUARE

for **-ing** meaning "going on, happening now" with doubling

Start in the middle square with the suffix **ing** and combine this part with the words in the other squares to build new words. Remember to double the final consonant of the words to which you attach the suffix **ing**. Write each word and a definition you can think of for it in the spaces provided at the bottom of the page.

dig	slip	win
run	**-ing**	swim
cut	plan	set

AFFIX ADDER

The suffix **-ing** means "going on, happening now."

When **–ing** is attached to a one-syllable word ending in a consonant with a single vowel in front of it, the consonant is doubled.

1. Write **ing** in the blank space after each word listed below and make a new word. Remember to double the last letter
2. Tell what you think the new word means.
3. Write a sentence using the new word.

We've done one for you:

SWAP means to trade

...so SWAPPING means trading.

Sentence: The teams were swapping baskets for the second half of the game.

1. SWAT means to hit at

...so SWAT_______ means ______________________________

Used in a sentence:

____

2. PROP means to set up

...so PROP_______ means ______________________________

Used in a sentence:

____

3. ROB means to steal from

...so ROB_______ means ______________________________

Used in a sentence:

____

4. BRAG means to boast about yourself

...so BRAG_______ means ______________________________

Used in a sentence:

____

5. RUN means to go fast on foot

...so RUN_______ means ___________________________________

Used in a sentence:

6. CRAM means to stuff full

...so CRAM_______ means___________________________________

Used in a sentence:

7. NOD means to agree with a shake of the head

...so NOD______ means ___________________________________

Used in a sentence:

8. SPIN means to go around fast

...so SPIN_______ means ___________________________________

Used in a sentence:

9. RIP means to tear

...so RIP______ means ___________________________________

Used in a sentence:

10. TUG means to pull at

...so TUG______ means ___________________________________

Used in a sentence:

MAGIC SQUARE

for -**ing** meaning "going on, happening now" with doubling

Select the best definition for each of the words in the **ing** with doubled consonant words family. Put the number of the definition in the proper space in the Magic Square box. If the numbers going up and down and the numbers going across all add up to the same thing, you have found the magic number!

WORDS

A. chopping
B. dripping
C. planning
D. hitting
E. bagging
F. setting
G. grinning
H. humming
I. rubbing

DEFINITIONS

1. striking
2. removing from
3. earning points in a game
4. singing with lips closed
5. losing water slowly
6. stroking with the hand
7. setting preparations for
8. putting down
9. cutting quickly
10. coming to an end
11. looking amused or sly
12. putting items into a sack

Magic Square Box

A.	B.	C.
D.	E.	F.
G.	H.	I.

Magic Number _____

Name ____________________

WORD SEARCH

Words with the suffix -ing, meaning "going on, happening," with doubling.

Find and circle all the words in the grid. Words can go across or up and down, straight or diagonally, forwards or backwards.

G	N	I	P	P	I	S	W	K	D	C	L	S	K	G	Y
G	N	I	P	P	A	T	W	N	N	B	Y	W	G	N	F
G	J	I	F	R	G	N	I	T	T	I	H	I	N	I	L
N	N	Y	N	M	I	Y	Q	G	M	X	T	M	I	G	L
B	D	I	Q	N	F	P	G	R	G	T	K	M	N	G	G
Y	G	G	M	J	I	R	P	N	R	S	J	I	N	A	E
D	L	N	M	M	I	W	I	I	E	W	M	N	I	R	T
T	I	R	I	N	A	M	R	T	N	M	N	G	P	B	T
H	R	G	N	M	M	L	T	K	A	G	N	K	S	F	I
V	U	I	G	I	M	I	S	R	Q	I	J	K	G	W	N
T	N	J	R	I	N	U	C	P	N	R	B	P	N	C	G
G	N	T	B	G	N	L	H	N	N	K	X	Z	I	R	Z
R	I	B	M	T	M	G	A	B	F	M	L	H	D	P	P
P	N	R	K	R	V	L	K	H	M	H	F	Y	D	M	N
K	G	K	V	B	P	R	U	B	B	I	N	G	O	W	M
Z	D	N	R	N	C	U	T	T	I	N	G	Y	N	T	H

bragging	humming	sipping
cramming	nodding	slamming
cutting	planning	spinning
digging	ripping	swimming
getting	rubbing	tapping
grinning	running	trimming
hitting	setting	winning

What's happening?

Fill in the blanks using the words below that all mean "going on, happening now."

Why do they mean going on or happening now? ______________________________

1. No one was ________________ today because sharks had been spotted in the water.
2. The car was ________________ on the invisible ice.
3. Cindy kept ________________ her eyes, not believing what she was seeing.
4. We were ________________ quickly across the hot sidewalk.
5. Mr. Casey was ________________ some flowers to take to the wedding.
6. They heard Zelda ________________ that she had beaten Nelda in chess.
7. The man was ________________ widely in the photograph because he had caught a big fish.
8. Everyone was ________________ Aunt Pauline at the family reunion.
9. Rain water was ________________ down the side of the house.
10. A big alligator was ________________ itself along the banks of the river.

Check off these words as you use them.

bragging	cutting	grinning	hopping	hugging
rubbing	running	skidding	sunning	swimming

SUFFIX SQUARE

for -**er** or -**or** meaning "a person or device that does"

The suffix spelled **er** is also sometimes spelled **or**. There is no reliable way to tell whether a word might be spelled with one ending or the other. When in doubt, look the word up in a dictionary. A less reliable trick is to try **er** on short, informal words, try **or** on longer, more formal words: bus "driver" versus locomotive "conductor." Start in the middle square and combine this part with the words in the other squares to build new words. Write each word and a definition you can think of for it in the spaces provided at the bottom of the page.

compact	count	test
paint	-**er** or -**or**?	collect
constrict	teach	instruct

AFFIX ADDER

The suffix **-er/-or** when added to a verb can change that verb into a word meaning "a person or device that does" whatever action is indicated by the verb.

1. Write **er** or **or** in the blank space after each word listed below and make a new word.
2. Tell what you think the new word means.
3. Write a sentence using the new word.

We've done one for you:

SLEEP means to rest soundly

...so SLEEP<u>ER</u> means <u>one who sleeps soundly.</u>

<u>Sentence</u>: Marika is such a sound sleeper it is hard to wake her up!

1. BUILD means to make from parts

...so BUILD___ means ______________________________

<u>Used in a sentence</u>:

____

2. HEAT means to make warm

...so HEAT ___ means ______________________________

<u>Used in a sentence</u>:

____

3. ACT means to do or perform

...so ACT___ means ______________________________

<u>Used in a sentence</u>:

____

4. TEACH means to guide or instruct

...so TEACH___ means ______________________________

<u>Used in a sentence</u>:

____

5. RECORD means to write down or copy

...so RECORD___ means ______________________________

Used in a sentence:

6. INVENT means to make an idea into something real

...so INVENT___ means ______________________________

Used in a sentence:

7. TWIST means to turn or to wind up

...so TWIST___ means ______________________________

Used in a sentence:

8. COOK means to prepare and heat for eating

...so COOK___ means ______________________________

Used in a sentence:

9. WASH means to clean in water

...so WASH___ means ______________________________

Used in a sentence:

10. TEST means to check on

...so TEST___ means ______________________________

Used in a sentence:

MAGIC SQUARE

for -**er**/-**or** meaning "a person or device that does"

Select the best definition for each of the words in the **er/or** family. Put the number of the definition in the proper space in the Magic Square box. If the numbers going up and down and the numbers going across all add up to the same thing, you have found the magic number!

WORDS

A. governor
B. mixer
C. reporter
D. visitor
E. actor
F. surveyor
G. orbiter
H. fastener
I. builder

DEFINITIONS

1. a device that joins together and holds firm
2. a person who comes to see you
3. a person who tells news stories
4. a person who looks over something or takes a poll
5. device that blends things
6. an object that circles around in space
7. a person who rules or guides a state
8. a person who makes houses
9. a person who does things on a stage

Magic Square Box

A.	B.	C.
D.	E.	F.
G.	H.	I.

Magic Number ______

Name ______________________

WORD SEARCH

Words with suffix -er or -or, meaning "a person or device that does"

Find and circle all the words in the grid. Words can go across or up and down, straight or diagonally, forwards or backwards.

L	M	Q	T	V	X	C	L	E	A	N	E	R	R	Y
D	C	R	E	T	R	O	F	M	O	C	Z	E	N	H
C	R	R	E	C	O	R	D	E	R	X	K	G	T	F
T	E	E	Q	P	K	Y	G	J	E	O	R	H	O	T
K	D	K	R	L	O	Z	J	M	O	E	P	R	V	R
R	I	C	T	O	N	R	P	C	L	B	G	F	E	T
R	T	O	K	C	T	L	T	L	O	A	K	T	C	L
E	O	L	Y	R	O	A	A	E	N	O	N	F	H	T
T	R	B	R	Y	E	C	N	I	R	I	L	R	N	E
A	X	K	E	N	N	N	Z	I	A	Q	W	E	V	A
E	L	R	T	Z	Q	E	E	P	L	P	K	B	R	C
H	M	K	N	Q	R	L	P	T	X	L	W	B	C	H
O	B	J	E	C	T	O	R	Z	S	T	O	V	L	E
Z	W	J	R	P	L	A	Y	E	R	A	B	P	V	R
R	E	A	D	E	R	R	E	X	I	F	F	B	P	F

blocker	employer	player
caller	fastener	pollinator
cleaner	fixer	reader
comforter	heater	recorder
cooker	objector	renter
cooler	organizer	reporter
creditor	painter	teacher

Action!

Fill in the blanks using the words below that all mean "a person or thing that does."

Why do they mean a person or thing that does? ________________________________

1. It is easier to study if you are a good _______________.
2. She has the best voice of any _______________ I've ever heard.
3. It helps to be a good _________________ if you work at a bank.
4. A ballerina is one type of ________________.
5. A great ________________ can make even boring subjects exciting!
6. Leonardo da Vinci was a great _______________, sculptor, and engineer.
7. My _________________ is slow, so it will take a while to make 10 copies.
8. My brother is a _________________ in the Navy.
9. Thomas Edison was a great __________________.
10. Even a great _________________ can't save a bad play!

Check off these words as you use them.

painter	inventor	counter	reader	teacher
printer	actor	singer	dancer	sailor

SUFFIX SQUARE

for **-like** meaning "similar to or resembling something"

Start in the middle square with the suffix **like** and combine this part with the words in the other squares to build new words. Write each word and a definition you can think of for it in the spaces provided at the bottom of the page.

business	cat	child
god	**-like**	war
lady	man	life

AFFIX ADDER

The suffix -like means "similar to or resembling something."

1. Write **like** in the blank space after each word listed below and make a new word.
2. Tell what you think the new word means.
3. Write a sentence using the new word.

We've done one for you:

CHILD means a young person
...so CHILDLIKE means similar to a child.

Sentence: The man's anger was inappropriate and childlike.

---

1. CARTOON means funny drawing
...so CARTOON ______ means ______________________________
Used in a sentence:

---

2. FOX means a sly and clever animal
...so FOX______ means ______________________________
Used in a sentence:

---

3. DREAM means ideas that occur in one's mind during sleep
...so DREAM______ means ______________________________
Used in a sentence:

---

4. STATESMAN means a person skilled at running a country
...so STATESMAN ______ means ______________________________
Used in a sentence:

---

5. LADY means a woman of refined behavior
...so LADY______ means ____
Used in a sentence:

---

6. MAZE means a confusing network of pathways
...so MAZE______ means ____
Used in a sentence:

---

7. PLAY means amusing recreation
...so PLAY______ means ____
Used in a sentence:

---

8. SPORTSMAN means a person who plays fair
...so SPORTSMAN______ means ____
Used in a sentence:

---

9. SPRING means the season of new growth and pleasant days
...so SPRING______ means ____
Used in a sentence:

---

10. TRANCE means a half-conscious state of mind
...so TRANCE ______ means ____
Used in a sentence:

MAGIC SQUARE

for **-like** meaning "similar to or resembling something"

Select the best definition for each of the words in the suffix **like** family. Put the number of the definition in the proper space in the Magic Square box. If the numbers going up and down and the numbers going across all add up to the same thing, you have found the magic number!

WORDS

A. swordlike
B. animallike
C. birdlike
D. boxlike
E. childlike
F. ghostlike
G. hornlike
H. lacelike
I. songlike

DEFINITIONS

1. like something alive
2. resembling one of our feathered friends
3. resembling a fluffy fabric with an open weave
4. resembling a square object to put things in
5. resembling the bony structure that some cows have on their head
6. resembling the spirit of a dead person
7. similar to a beast
8. resembling a young person
9. resembling something long and sharp
10. resembling pretty music

Magic Square Box

A.	B.	C.
D.	E.	F.
G.	H.	I.

Magic Number ______

Name ______________________

WORD SEARCH

Words with the suffix -like, meaning "similar to or resembling something"

Find and circle all the words in the grid. Words can go across or up and down, straight or diagonally, forwards or backwards.

L	Z	F	B	B	U	S	I	N	E	S	S	L	I	K	E	L	S	L
S	S	P	O	R	T	S	M	A	N	L	I	K	E	N	E	T	P	B
T	T	T	N	W	I	N	T	E	R	L	I	K	E	N	K	L	R	V
A	H	K	M	Z	J	E	K	I	L	E	Z	A	M	F	I	D	I	K
T	L	Y	P	C	E	L	T	Z	T	L	N	Q	V	F	L	C	N	K
E	N	R	K	G	K	Q	J	E	R	D	Q	D	E	Y	T	H	G	W
S	H	T	H	W	I	F	B	R	K	Q	R	L	G	T	N	C	L	T
M	E	H	S	G	L	Z	B	D	R	I	I	E	N	X	A	Z	I	T
A	K	R	W	M	T	W	N	C	S	K	L	M	A	E	L	H	K	K
N	I	E	O	R	L	R	Y	K	E	U	T	E	K	M	P	R	E	D
L	L	A	R	Y	U	M	Z	H	E	X	M	I	C	J	L	S	V	N
I	R	D	D	L	D	R	H	K	Y	E	L	M	M	N	T	I	G	Y
K	A	L	L	A	A	L	I	W	R	P	K	T	E	A	A	V	K	P
E	W	I	I	D	Z	L	C	D	E	R	N	I	G	R	X	R	K	E
M	H	K	K	Y	D	X	W	E	Y	C	R	E	L	T	L	V	T	R
R	C	E	E	L	D	W	L	X	K	M	L	Z	D	Y	V	I	P	R
D	N	J	I	I	T	S	L	M	M	I	N	Z	M	C	A	T	K	X
T	K	H	K	K	F	H	T	E	K	I	L	Y	O	T	T	L	R	E
M	C	K	N	E	L	K	G	E	B	C	N	L	R	Y	Y	Y	P	N

adultlike	plantlike	summerlike
businesslike	playlike	swordlike
childlike	sleeplike	threadlike
dreamlike	sportsmanlike	toylike
ladylike	springlike	trancelike
lifelike	stagelike	warlike
mazelike	statesmanlike	winterlike

COPYCAT!

Fill in the blanks using the words at the bottom of the page that all mean "similar to or resembling something."
Why do they mean similar to or resembling something? ____________________

1. John and Bo have quick, ____________ reflexes when they hear a refrigerator door open.

2. The calm and _______________ landscape in the painting was beautiful.

3. Although the visiting team lost, they were ______________ and congratulated us.

4. A _______________ politician will put the country ahead of party interests.

5. In a _____________ fit of anger, Caroline threw the flowerpot up against the wall.

6. Some kind of long, thin, _______________ alga was growing in the pond.

7. Hoping to get the job, Shaun dressed in a _______________ manner.

8. The noisy, _______________ behavior of the teenagers in the restaurant disturbed others.

9. The bananas in the painting are so _______________ that you want to eat one.

10. The _______________ day in January made us want to lie in the sun.

Check off these words as you use them.

businesslike	catlike	childlike	dreamlike	lifelike
sportsmanlike	springlike	statesmanlike	threadlike	warlike

SUFFIX SQUARE

for -**less** meaning "without; not having"

Start in the middle square with the suffix **less** and combine this part with the words in the other squares to build new words. Write each word and a definition you can think of for it in the spaces provided at the bottom of the page.

help	end	win
clue	**-less**	harm
care	fear	rest

AFFIX ADDER

The suffix -less means "without; not having."

1. Write **less** in the blank space in front of each word listed below and make a new word.
2. Tell what you think the new word means.
3. Write a sentence using the new word.

We've done one for you:

HOPE means wish or expectation
...so HOPELESS means without expectation.

Sentence: With the score 38-0, it was hopeless to think our team could win.

1. END means a stop
...so END______ means ______________________________

Used in a sentence:

2. RIM means a frame of hard material
...so RIM______ means ______________________________

Used in a sentence:

3. JOB means a place of work or a task
...so JOB______ means ______________________________

Used in a sentence:

4. FORM means shape
...so FORM______ means ______________________________

Used in a sentence:

5. TOOTH means a hard structure in the mouth for biting and chewing
...so TOOTH______ means ___________________________________

Used in a sentence:

6. FLAW means weakness or defect
...so FLAW______ means ___________________________________

Used in a sentence:

7. NAME means whatever something or someone is called by
...so NAME______ means ___________________________________

Used in a sentence:

8. MOON refers to the brightly shining satellite of a planet
...so MOON______ means ___________________________________

Used in a sentence:

9. FAITH means confident belief in
...so FAITH______ means ___________________________________

10. HOME means a place or dwelling where one lives
...so HOME______ means ___________________________________

Used in a sentence:

MAGIC SQUARE

for **-less** meaning "without; not having"

Select the best definition for each of the words in the **less** family. Put the number of the definition in the proper space in the Magic Square box. If the numbers going up and down and the numbers going across all add up to the same thing, you have found the magic number!

WORDS

A. aimless
B. joyless
C. winless
D. harmless
E. needless
F. timeless
G. selfless
H. luckless
I. careless

DEFINITIONS

1. without fortune
2. without hurt
3. without a victory
4. without beginning or end
5. without happiness
6. not having concern for oneself
7. without purpose or direction
8. without concern about making a mistake
9. without being required

Magic Square Box

A.	B.	C.
D.	E.	F.
G.	H.	I.

Magic Number ______

Name ____________________

WORD SEARCH

Words with the suffix -less, meaning "without; not having"

Find and circle the words in the grid. Words can go across or up and down, straight or diagonally, forwards or backwards.

S	M	L	K	T	R	E	E	L	E	S	S	N	L	S	N
J	S	M	Z	B	H	O	M	E	L	E	S	S	S	C	N
M	B	E	M	K	S	J	R	B	B	Z	K	E	L	M	S
X	R	R	L	F	S	Q	Y	K	D	S	L	U	M	S	Q
F	D	L	Y	P	E	D	V	X	S	N	E	L	E	Z	P
L	A	S	R	M	L	D	Z	E	U	L	I	L	G	S	R
A	R	C	S	N	W	E	L	S	E	F	D	N	M	S	Y
S	G	L	E	E	A	T	H	S	E	E	G	V	F	E	H
S	C	E	N	L	L	M	S	L	E	R	N	X	N	L	A
E	M	J	L	A	E	T	E	N	K	R	C	L	N	T	I
L	M	O	S	E	T	S	S	E	L	K	C	U	L	O	R
E	Q	Y	Z	D	S	S	S	E	L	M	R	A	H	P	L
M	M	L	H	V	R	S	G	X	R	L	N	L	P	S	E
A	R	E	S	S	E	L	H	T	O	O	T	M	T	V	S
N	K	S	R	A	I	M	L	E	S	S	D	P	L	M	S
X	B	S	C	O	R	D	L	E	S	S	F	Y	V	Z	X

ageless	helpless	needless
aimless	homeless	restless
clueless	joyless	saltless
cordless	lawless	spotless
faceless	lifeless	sunless
hairless	luckless	toothless
harmless	nameless	treeless

WITHOUT!

Fill in the blanks using the words below that all mean "without or not having something."
Why do they mean without or not having something? ______________________________

1. The witness chooses to remain ________________ for his own protection.
2. Because they are ________________, the eyeglasses seem almost invisible.
3. ________________ tools do not need to be plugged in, because they use batteries.
4. Our ________________ leader brought us through very tough times.
5. Can you tell the ________________ snakes from the ones that are poisonous?
6. There was a lot of ________________ waste of time at the meeting.
7. Jo was ________________ and lost control of the car for a second.
8. Because it is still hot in October, it seems that this summer is ________________.
9. Donna gave a ________________ recitation of The Gettysburg Address.
10. With no fixed address, ________________ people have a hard time getting a job.

Check off these words as you use them.

careless	cordless	endless	fearless	flawless
harmless	homeless	nameless	needless	rimless

PREFIX SQUARE

for **in-** meaning "in or into"

Start in the middle square with the prefix **in** and combine this part with the words in the other squares to build new words. Write each word and a definition you can think of for it in the spaces provided at the bottom of the page.

coming	doors	laid
fill	**in-**	set
rush	quest	going

AFFIX ADDER

This prefix in- means "in or into."

1. Write **in** in the blank space in front of each word listed below and make a new word.
2. Tell what you think the new word means.
3. Write a sentence using the new word.

We've done one for you:

BOUND means headed in a specific direction

...so IN BOUND means headed in.

Sentence: I waited at the airport for my mother's inbound flight.

1. DOOR refers to an entrance to a building
   ...so ____ DOOR means ____________________
   Used in a sentence:

2. CURVED means smoothly bent
   ...so ____ CURVED means ____________________
   Used in a sentence:

3. COMING means arriving
   ...so ____ COMING means ____________________
   Used in a sentence:

4. FIELD means place where a game takes place
   ...so ____ FIELD means ____________________
   Used in a sentence:

5. SIGHT means look

...so ____ SIGHT means ______________________________

Used in a sentence:

6. FLOW means to move smoothly

...so ____ FLOW means ______________________________

Used in a sentence:

7. DWELL means to exist

...so ____ DWELL means ______________________________

Used in a sentence:

8. LAND means any part of the earth not covered by water

...so ____ LAND means ______________________________

Used in a sentence:

9. PUT means to place

...so ____ PUT means ______________________________

Used in a sentence:

10. RUSH means to hurry or move swiftly

...so ____ RUSH means ______________________________

Used in a sentence:

MAGIC SQUARE

for **in**- meaning "in or into"

Select the best definition for each of the words in the **in** (in) family. Put the number of the definition in the proper space in the Magic Square box. If the numbers going up and down and the numbers going across all add up to the same thing, you have found the magic number!

WORDS

A. incline
B. infighting
C. indoors
D. inrush
E. inlaid
F. income
G. inland
H. inspect
I. inborn

DEFINITIONS

1. given at birth
2. set down as decoration into a surface
3. to lean in, slant, or slope
4. a fast pouring in, like water from a storm
5. inside a building
6. to look into closely
7. quarrels among insiders, friends, or family members
8. a place farther in from the beach
9. money a person brings in or earns

Magic Square Box

A.	B.	C.
D.	E.	F.
G.	H.	I.

Magic Number ______

Name ____________________________

WORD SEARCH

Words with the prefix in- meaning "in"

Find and circle all the words in the grid. Words can go across or up and down, straight or diagonally, forwards or backwards.

G	I	D	L	I	V	T	R	R	D	I	C	G	T	T
N	N	J	I	F	N	V	S	I	Y	N	N	N	F	Q
I	M	X	N	R	M	F	A	E	T	J	E	L	C	F
O	O	B	S	Y	N	L	I	N	U	D	V	I	E	I
G	S	K	E	R	N	W	N	E	N	Q	N	F	N	T
N	T	M	T	I	Y	F	O	I	L	F	N	S	T	M
I	N	D	O	O	R	S	C	R	L	D	C	I	M	D
I	D	I	L	K	N	H	H	O	G	R	K	E	L	R
N	T	N	N	R	L	Y	W	E	I	N	L	M	M	A
F	K	K	Z	S	Q	C	D	B	M	P	I	O	Z	W
L	Q	N	K	D	P	A	E	N	M	Q	Z	C	W	N
A	P	M	T	Z	V	I	N	L	A	N	D	N	R	I
T	Z	Q	B	N	J	R	R	N	Y	L	J	I	L	X
E	G	D	I	N	J	N	K	E	D	L	O	F	N	I
W	I	N	S	T	A	L	L	H	S	U	R	N	I	R

income	ingoing	inrush
indent	ingrown	inscribe
indoors	inlaid	inset
infield	inland	inspire
inflate	inlet	install
inflow	inmost	invade
infold	inquest	inward

What Are You Into?

Fill in the blanks using the words below that all mean "in or into."

Why do they mean in or into? ______________________________

1. During a flood, the ____________ of water causes a lot of damage.
2. Denver Colorado is far ____________ from the coast of California.
3. An argument between family members is also called ____________.
4. If it rains, our meeting will be held ____________.
5. When you see inside how someone thinks, it is an ____________.
6. We had to wait at the airport for Joe's ____________ flight.
7. Money a person brings in or earns is called ____________.
8. A piece of metal bent inward is ____________.
9. I ____________ money by putting it into something that I hope will give more back.
10. I like boats with ____________ motors because you can't see them.

Check off these words as you use them.

insight	income	infighting	incurved	invest
incoming	inflow	inboard	indoors	inland

PREFIX SQUARE

for **in**- meaning "not"

Start in the middle square with the prefix **in** and combine this part with the words in the other squares to build new words. Write each word and a definition you can think of for it in the spaces provided at the bottom of the page.

correct	exact	finite
edible	**in-**	visible
sane	complete	active

AFFIX ADDER

This prefix in- means "not."

1. Write **in** in the blank space in front of each word listed below and make a new word.
2. Tell what you think the new word means.
3. Write a sentence using the new word.

We've done one for you:

VALID means true

...so <u>IN</u>VALID means <u>not true.</u>

<u>Sentence</u>: Joey lied, so his answer was invalid.

1. ACTIVE means doing, in process

...so ____ ACTIVE means ______________________________

<u>Used in a sentence</u>:

____

2. CONVENIENT means easy

...so ____ CONVENIENT means ______________________________

<u>Used in a sentence</u>:

____

3. CORRECT means right

...so ____ CORRECT means ______________________________

<u>Used in a sentence</u>:

____

4. DIRECT means toward a definite place

...so ____ DIRECT means ______________________________

<u>Used in a sentence</u>:

____

5. FORMAL means having a definite shape or style
...so ____ FORMAL means ______________________________
Used in a sentence:

6. HUMAN means like a person
...so ____ HUMAN means ______________________________
Used in a sentence:

7. OFFENSIVE means nasty or smelly
...so ____ OFFENSIVE means ______________________________
Used in a sentence:

8. ORGANIC means natural
...so ____ ORGANIC means ______________________________
Used in a sentence:

9. SECURE means feeling safe
...so ____ SECURE means ______________________________
Used in a sentence:

10. VISIBLE means able to be seen
...so ____ VISIBLE means ______________________________
Used in a sentence:

MAGIC SQUARE

for **in**- meaning "not"

Select the best definition for each of the words in the **in** (not) family. Put the number of the definition in the proper space in the Magic Square box. If the numbers going up and down and the numbers going across all add up to the same thing, you have found the magic number!

WORDS

A. inactive
B. inconsiderate
C. inhuman
D. insecure
E. insincere
F. incomplete
G. incorrect
H. insignificant
I. inflexible

DEFINITIONS

1. not easily bent or changed; rigid
2. not safe or comfortable
3. not thoughtful or polite
4. not truthful
5. not like a person
6. not right
7. not doing anything
8. not important
9. not finished

Magic Square Box

A.	B.	C.
D.	E.	F.
G.	H.	I.

Magic Number ______

Name ____________________________

WORD SEARCH

Words with the prefix in- meaning "not"

Find and circle all the words in the grid. Words can go across or up and down, straight or diagonally, forwards or backwards.

```
L M C R T R M X V I M N T W Y C F Z I L E
V W X S U O R E M U N N I G Q N V N K T L
G X K H F K C I M Y F E P D W N C W E Z B
B B W L Q M N M K H L X Q B V R R L N C A
K N V A D D G T C C M T E U E F P F L Z R
V L K M I B E F M P X N N D A M Z H W K E
K I X R T Z C T L F A T I N O L T M R D M
K N E O C J D T A S M B J C Y C I M C N U
M C C F E K J L N R L P N R A F N T P H N
T O V N R E T I H E E I T X P M F M Y P N
K N I I R V B D D M D D E Y C G D N N C I
Y V N V O I B L E T I N I F N I B N V T M
N E E C C S I R T C I N E S C A P A B L E
R N F B N N L N D M L N X P N W P G V Y Q
F I F B I E I N A C T I O N E O R R V R V
T E E T Y P L T R C G Z N K Y D C C H H Q
W N C Y C X R Z N W T L M H T F N N K H D
N T T N M E N K L W N I K K K J M I I T Y
M K I P C N L G M R W W V N X H J K P J M
H M V D J I N V I S I B L E B W Y V N H K
Y Y E J H J G E L B A B I R C S E D N I H
```

inaction	independent	inexpensive
inactive	indescribable	infinite
incomplete	indirect	informal
inconsiderate	ineffective	innumerable
inconvenient	inequality	innumerous
incorrect	inescapable	insane
incredible	inexact	invisible

Not In the Mood

Fill in the blanks using the words below that all mean "not."

Why do they mean <u>not</u>? ______________________________

1. If I am _______________, it means you can't see me.
2. Animals who are not human are_______________.
3. You don't get credit if you give an _______________ answer.
4. If you just sit around and are _______________, you won't be healthy.
5. You can go straight or take the _______________ way to get somewhere.
6. If something is _______________ it does not cost a lot.
7. If you have an _______________ to do something, it means you can't do it.
8. If something is not finished, it is _______________.
9. If something is _______________, it cannot be divided into smaller parts.
10. If your answer is not exactly right, it is _______________

<u>Check off these words as you use them</u>.

inactive	inhuman	invisible	indivisible	indirect
inability	inexpensive	incomplete	incorrect	inexact

SUFFIX SQUARE

for **-ed** meaning "did before now, in the past" with dropped **e**

Start in the middle square with the suffix **ed** and combine this part with the words in the other squares to build new words. Remember to drop the final **e** of the words to which you attach the suffix **ed**. Write each word and a definition you can think of for it in the spaces provided at the bottom of the page.

bake	joke	like
name	**-ed**	move
dance	guide	paste

AFFIX ADDER

The suffix -ed means "did before now, in the past."

When –ed is attached to a word ending with the letter e, the ending e is dropped.

1. Draw a line through the final letter **e** of each of the words below.
2. Write **ed** in the blank space after each word listed below and make a new word.
3. Tell what you think the new word means.
4. Write a sentence using the new word.

We've done one for you:

CLOSE means to shut

...so CLOS~~E~~ED means shut in the past.

Sentence: She closed the door quietly after she saw the baby was asleep.

1. ERASE means to wipe clean

...so ERASE_____ means ____________________

Used in a sentence:

2. RAISE means to lift up

...so RAISE_____ means ____________________

Used in a sentence:

3. SCORE means to make points in a game

...so SCORE_____ means ____________________

Used in a sentence:

4. SMILE means to curve the mouth upward and look pleasant
...so SMILE_____ means ______________________________
Used in a sentence:

5. VOTE means to choose
...so VOTE_____ means ______________________________
Used in a sentence:

6. TRADE means to swap
...so TRADE_____ means______________________________
Used in a sentence:

7. AMAZE means to surprise with awe
...so AMAZE_____ means ______________________________
Used in a sentence:

8. PLACE means to put in a location
...so PLACE_____ means ______________________________
Used in a sentence:

9. JUDGE means to decide or rate
...so JUDGE_____ means ______________________________
Used in a sentence:

10. AMUSE means to humor or make laugh
...so AMUSE_____ means ______________________________
Used in a sentence:

MAGIC SQUARE

for -**ed** meaning "did before now, in the past" with dropped **e**

Select the best definition for each of the words in the **ed** with dropped **e** family. Put the number of the definition in the proper space in the Magic Square box. If the numbers going up and down and the numbers going across all add up to the same thing, you have found the magic number!

WORDS

A. taped
B. saved
C. arranged
D. traded
E. pledged
F. achieved
G. improved
H. tamed
I. behaved

DEFINITIONS

1. surprised with awe
2. put into good, neat order
3. calmed and made comfortable in a house
4. swapped
5. made better
6. won or succeeded
7. rescued or held back for later use
8. made a promise
9. put onto film for viewing later
10. acted in a proper way

Magic Square Box

A.	B.	C.
D.	E.	F.
G.	H.	I.

Magic Number _____

Name ___________________________

WORD SEARCH

Words with the suffix -ed, meaning "happened before now, in the past," with dropped e.

Find and circle all the words in the grid. Words can go across or up and down, straight or diagonally, forwards or backwards.

B	J	L	R	D	F	D	D	E	S	I	A	R
Y	E	V	O	T	E	D	P	J	P	H	J	C
M	L	H	B	P	D	V	E	L	Y	P	E	L
J	T	N	A	M	E	D	O	M	A	R	T	O
T	P	T	R	V	V	M	Q	R	A	C	X	S
F	J	S	A	D	E	V	M	S	P	T	E	E
X	N	M	C	K	I	D	E	D	Q	M	D	D
D	D	I	E	N	H	D	E	D	P	E	I	Q
E	E	L	D	M	C	D	E	A	V	X	G	C
R	G	E	R	T	A	Z	S	O	Z	B	V	T
O	D	D	Y	R	A	T	M	L	W	D	Q	M
C	U	R	T	M	E	A	R	R	I	V	E	D
S	J	T	A	D	D	E	D	I	U	G	B	D

achieved	improved	raised
amazed	judged	scored
arrived	moved	smiled
behaved	named	tamed
closed	pasted	taped
erased	placed	traded
guided	raced	voted

Drop It!

Fill in the blanks using the words below that all mean "did an action in the past."

Why do they mean did something in the past? ______________________________

1. Marvin wrote his name in the sand, but the waves ______________ it.

2. Earl, the umpire, ______________ that the ball was a foul.

3. With paper-safe glue, Ruth ______________ the photographs in an album.

4. Raymond ______________ the highest score on the spelling test.

5. Naomi ______________ the books on her shelf in alphabetic order.

6. The tour guide commented on how well the class ______________ on the trip to the caverns.

7. "Jane, your vocabulary has ______________ so much during this year," said her teacher.

8. Blair was ______________ by the good-natured jokes that his friends told about him.

9. Jean ______________ three pumpkin pies for the Thanksgiving dessert.

10. Polly ______________ and sang in the talent show that our school held.

Check off these words as you use them.

achieved	amused	arranged	baked	behaved
danced	erased	improved	judged	pasted

SUFFIX SQUARE

for -**ing** meaning "going on, happening" with dropped **e**

Start in the middle square with the suffix **ing** and combine this part with the words in the other squares to build new words. Remember to drop the final **e** of the words to which you attach the suffix **ing**. Write each word and a definition you can think of for it in the spaces provided at the bottom of the page.

write	hope	come
excite	**-ing**	make
hike	wade	ride

AFFIX ADDER

The suffix **-ing** means "going on, happening."

When –**ing** is attached to a word ending with the letter **e**, the ending **e** is dropped.

1. Draw a line through the final letter **e** of each of the words below.
2. Write **ing** in the blank space after each word listed below and make a new word.
3. Tell what you think the new word means.
4. Write a sentence using the new word.

We've done one for you:

TYPE means to print using a keyboard
...so TYP~~E~~ING means printing using a keyboard.

Sentence: *We were typing our names at the computer.*

1. DANCE means to move in rhythm
...so DANCE___ means ______________________
Used in a sentence:

2. CARE means to have concern
...so CARE___ means ______________________
Used in a sentence:

3. BITE means to use the teeth
...so BITE___ means ______________________
Used in a sentence:

4. HIDE means to cover up or conceal
...so HIDE___ means ____________________________________
Used in a sentence:

5. JOKE means to be silly or have fun
...so JOKE___ means ____________________________________
Used in a sentence:

6. BAKE means to cook with heat
...so BAKE___ means ____________________________________
Used in a sentence:

7. PLACE means to put in a location
...so PLACE___ means ____________________________________
Used in a sentence:

8. NAME means to give a title to
...so NAME___ means ____________________________________
Used in a sentence:

9. TRACE means to follow around an outline
...so TRACE___ means ____________________________________
Used in a sentence:

10. TIRE means to bore or wear out
...so TIRE___ means ____________________________________
Used in a sentence:

MAGIC SQUARE

for -**ing** meaning "going on, happening" with dropped **e**

Select the best definition for each of the words in the **ing** with dropped **e** family. Put the number of the definition in the proper space in the Magic Square box. If the numbers going up and down and the numbers going across all add up to the same thing, you have found the magic number!

WORDS

A. taking
B. fading
C. tiring
D. forcing
E. deciding
F. relieving
G. completing
H. reversing
I. scoring

DEFINITIONS

1. moving in water
2. removing from
3. earning points in a game
4. making a judgment
5. going in the opposite direction
6. putting pressure on
7. wearing out
8. making easier
9. getting lighter or more faint
10. coming to an end

Magic Square Box

A.	B.	C.
D.	E.	F.
G.	H.	I.

Name ______________________

WORD SEARCH

Words with the suffix -ing, meaning "going on, happening," with dropped e.

Find and circle all the words in the grid. Words can go across or up and down, straight or diagonally, forwards or backwards.

R	H	O	P	I	N	G	T	E	W	D	K	T
I	G	G	M	R	F	I	X	N	X	X	L	G
D	N	P	N	Y	R	C	G	N	I	D	A	W
I	I	H	G	I	I	C	C	A	R	I	N	G
N	K	X	N	T	C	G	O	P	R	N	C	L
G	A	G	I	D	G	R	R	M	P	L	R	T
G	B	N	P	A	N	N	O	L	I	G	G	W
N	G	A	Y	N	I	M	A	F	N	N	G	R
I	K	M	T	C	D	C	A	I	I	N	G	I
K	T	I	R	I	I	X	T	K	I	G	L	T
A	V	N	F	N	H	I	O	K	I	Y	M	I
T	V	G	G	G	B	J	I	N	F	N	G	N
G	N	I	D	A	F	H	R	J	R	M	G	G

baking	forcing	placing
biting	hiding	riding
caring	hiking	taking
coming	hoping	tiring
dancing	joking	typing
exciting	making	wading
fading	naming	writing

Drop It – Part 2!

Fill in the blanks using the words below that all mean "going on or happening."

Why do they mean going on or happening? ______________________________

1. Both the teachers and the students were ______________ that it would snow.
2. Michaela was ______________ a gift from the class to their friend in the hospital.
3. Dawn loves ______________ poetry and short stories.
4. The sun was ______________ our skin on the beach, so we got an umbrella.
5. A Nobel Prize winner will be ______________ to our school next week.
6. The mother cat was ______________ her kittens in the closet.
7. For their projects, Mia was ______________ a mosaic and Pia was preparing pasta.
8. The elephants were ______________ in the cool water.
9. Sal said that he was ______________ for his little sister and couldn't leave the house.
10. People were ______________ joyfully in the streets when they heard the good news.

Check off these words as you use them.

baking	caring	coming	dancing	hiding
hoping	making	taking	wading	writing